Good Morning, Beautiful

Winning the Battle Over Seizures

D1595918

Good Morning, Beautiful

Winning the Battle Over Seizures

by

Paulette George

Ambassador International

GREENVILLE, SOUTH CAROLINA & BELFAST, NORTHERN IRELAND

www.ambassador-international.com

Good Morning Beautiful

Winning the Battle Over Seizures

Printed in the United States of America

ISBN 978-1-935507-12-3

Cover Design & Page Layout by David Siglin of A&E Media

All photos copyright Mike Tanner: http://stmikesphotos.wmpwonline.com.

Steve Holy. "Good Morning Beautiful." Blue Moon. Curb Records, 2001. CD.

AMBASSADOR INTERNATIONAL
Emerald House
427 Wade Hampton Blvd.
Greenville, SC 29609, USA
www.ambassador-international.com

AMBASSADOR PUBLICATIONS
Providence House
Ardenlee Street
Belfast, BT6 8QJ, Northern Ireland, UK
www.ambassador-productions.com

The colophon is a trademark of Ambassador

Dedication

For Christina, baby girl I am so proud of you for allowing your story to be shared to help others.

And Mathew—our fearless prayer warrior who reminds us of the siblings trundled along during the storm.

And to Larry, for our beautiful children and your arm whenever I need help standing strong.

And for all whose lives have been brushed by the winds of seizures. Don't give up.

Remembrances

WE SHALL NEVER FORGET THE little ones and their families whose lives have touched ours and inspired me to continue seeking publishing.

Kayden Kemp
Carlie Jae Morgan
Katlin Laurene Ringhofer
W. Warren Stone

I could not finish this book without remembering Tré our five month old nephew who died due to a fire six months after Christina's brain surgery.

Our pastor once said, "God never wastes a tear." We stand with you on the promises in scripture. There will come a day when we will see our loved ones again and God will wipe away all the tears.

Acknowledgements

WHEN I GOT STUCK IN a road-block of thought, just an email away there was help from a friend and writer who patiently read every word and offered his gift of colors to help paint the scenes more vividly for the reader. His help rerouted the course, and brought me out of the jam. I don't know what I would have done without his help.

Mark Jedrzejczyk. You are talented. Thank you a million times over. Get your pen ready, I want a signed copy of your first book— I know it will be a captivating read!

Karen Brown, Barbara Dega, Barb Plotsky, Heather Redic, Cathy Taylor and Betsy Williams. Before a contract was signed, you were faithful in praying. As I wrote some of the more emotional chapters, it was a struggle to finish, but when the right combination of words inked the page, I knew it was because of your prayers—I thank God for you—I love you guys.

Heather, Rachel, Tonya, Megan, Mandi and Krissy. Thank you for your suggestions edits, comments and support.

Les Stobbe. I know you weren't aware of this, but it wasn't just the prompting from a friend who told you I had a story, but her kick from under the table which prompted me to share our story with you. Thank you for listening. It is an honor to work with you.

Jennifer. Thanks for the kick, my friend.

Cathy Weinke. Thank you for mentoring me in writing, critiquing and praying for us.

Steve Holy, Steve Braun and the Holy-ite crew. You guys are the best! Thank you for being there through the highs and lows when we struggled to dance around it all.

Jim Abrahams and the Charlie Foundation. If it wasn't for "First Do No Harm," we would never have heard of the ketogenic diet—there are no words to express our gratitude.

Dr. Jeffrey Buchhalter. Thank you for never giving up on the fight for seizure freedom.

Pastor Brian Henry. Thank you for nurturing our family's faith over the past several years, and supporting the tug I felt to write our story with your encouragement, direction and prayers.

Pastor Dave Nelson. For your reminder that none of us are perfect, and where we stand with God is measured by one thing: Grace. Thank you—it takes a load off.

Ambassador International. Thank you for reading our story and believing in the vision to help others with it. David the pages look amazing, and you crafted the perfect face to our story in the cover design. I'm still in awe at how you did that. Thank you for your gift of design.

My husband: Larry and our children, Mathew and Christina. While I worked in my office, Larry cooked Thanksgiving dinner—without my help, as I finished the last few pages of this book. The kids helped set the table and when the turkey came from the oven we all laughed until we cried—it was cooked upside down. Honey thank you, for cooking and being my partner through it all, and kids, thank you for giving up mom time. I love you more.

And God, Jehovah-Rapha. Thank you for blessing us with Children. What a boring place the world would be without them. We pray you use this story to help others.

Foreword

by Dr. Jeffrey Buchhalter
Chief, Division of Pediatric Neurology
Director, Pediatric Comprehensive Epilepsy Program
Phoenix Children's Hospital

SEVERAL YEARS AGO, I BECAME aware of a cartoon titled "Never Give Up". It depicted a long legged white feathered stork standing in a pond with the front half of a frog in its beak. However, the frog wrapped its green front legs around the bird's neck choking it so the frog could not be swallowed. This book *Good Morning, Beautiful*, is emblematic of the human spirit's desire to never give up. It is a work of deep pain, hope, joy and faith that could only have been written by Christina's mother.

I first met little Christina through the steel bars of a hospital crib. She was just one year old. Her parents were like most parents as they are going through the reality of a critically ill child, for whom an answer was not yet in sight. They were bedraggled, burnt-out and worried. What they didn't know was that their advocacy for their daughter was going to change her story from nightmare to hope. Thus began our relationship more than a decade ago.

Many of my patients are similar to Christina whose life was afflicted with epilepsy, a relentless disorder that can strike at any age, but the first peak incidence is in the first year of life. She endured sudden, unpredictable and potentially life-threatening seizures that continued for years. Imagine her distress and the consuming fear of her parents.

In this context when a family confronts a medical care environment that fails to meet the needs of the child or parents, what can they do? As one who has devoted his professional life to the care of children with epilepsy, I can tell you that this occurs not out of lack of concern on the part of health care providers, but lack of expertise and familiarity. This book shares the journey of how one family learned what they could do. Its intent is to impact others lives and inspire them to do the same as families must assume responsibility for care.

Christina's journey included a treatment for seizures that has been in use since the 1920's, the ketogenic diet. With the advent of more "modern" medication, expertise in using the diet became restricted to relatively few centers. However, as a member of the Scientific Advisory Board of the Charlie Foundation, I can attest to the importance of this treatment modality in the 21st century.

To imply that this story is simply about seizures, treatments, and technology would be only not a superficial recount of what took place. It is much more of a real, open, honest account of what a family confronted with a serious medical condition can do. Christina's story of persistence, love, faith and prayer has touched and enhanced the lives of countless others. It is my honor to be one of those she and her family have touched.

One of the messages of Christina's story is that parents and health care providers must be like that frog—we must never give up insisting that each child receive the optimal care. I knew how the story started, evolved and ended prior to reading this text. And yet, it was like reading a new story with all of the impact involved in the tragedy, courage, determination and hope experienced. We are all healed in some way by Christina's life and it has only just begun.

Table of Contents

PAULETTE GEORGE'S WONDERFULLY WRITTEN *Good Morning, Beautiful* is more than an emotional insight into a family's battle with epilepsy, more than a compelling argument for the ketogenic diet, and more than just hope that victory can happen. It offers strength to persevere and inspiration for parent empowerment.

—JIM ABRAHAMS
The Charlie Foundation To Help Cure Pediatric Epilepsy.

ALL OF US PARENTS FEAR THE DAY the doctor tells us something is terribly wrong with one of our children. My friend Paulette George and her husband lived this fear. *Good Morning Beautiful* is their heartfelt story of faith. You will be challenged, encouraged, and moved to tears as you read Paulette's raw but inspiring journey. This book is destined to move your heart toward the Heavenly Father.

—DANIEL DARLING
Senior Pastor, Gages Lake Bible Church, columnist for Crosswalk.com, and author of Teen People of the Bible, and Crash Course, Forming a Faith Foundation for Life.

I'VE SEEN CHRISTINA AS SHE GREW and saw the impossible become reality. Her story has touched me, and shows us all the power of music. I highly recommend this book, not just because my music played a role in this story, but because of its message of courage, faith and love of family.

—STEVE HOLY
National Recording Artist, Curb Records.

Preface

THE 727 BANKED, ROUTING IT northbound for Minneapolis. Through the window the wing lowered as stars hung in the clear night sky against the darkness. Some sparkled as a precious gem does when hit by light. Relief at the cloudless sky, rendering a smooth flight, didn't come as it should. An inner storm was raging, bringing with it gusts of fear and panic.

A tear slipped out from already exhausted eyes and began to run down my cheek. Glancing around, the passengers were reading or talking to the persons next to them. Not wanting anyone to notice, I nonchalantly brushed the tear away. Long, sleepless nights in the hospital left my eyes burning and rimmed in red. As I slid my finger into the hand of my tiny daughter, she moved hers slightly to accommodate. Looking more like an infant than the toddler she was supposed to be, below fine blonde curls, her face was thin and pale. Her sea blue eyes were open but showing no sign of what they were fixed on. She was still and quiet. Capped IVs ran into each arm and bruises lingered near them, as well as areas of unsuccessful attempts at placements and blood draws. Tiny veins were not meant for this.

When the tall brunette flight attendant who had seated us before anyone boarded came by, I knew she was being kind by offering food. "Can your baby have anything?"

Holding back emotion, I thanked her and said no. It wasn't just the special diet we were feeding Christina or the relentless seizures. Truth is, she had not eaten nor drunk anything on her own for weeks. First, she wouldn't finish her meal. She gagged when my husband or I tried to force drops of formula into her mouth with a syringe. The nurses also tried to feed her this way, without success. Prescribed much later than it should have, the feeding tube running into her nose held in place with tape was keeping her alive. The tube ran into a portable pump filled with her "special" formula, equipped to sling over my shoulder for transporting her. For now, it sat at the floor near my feet.

Daunting thoughts crept through my mind. *Could there be a genetic disorder or cancer that has been missed? Why is this happening to us? God, this must be a cruel joke, after all we went through to have children. How could this be?*

Closing my eyes, I held them shut in hopes this was just a bad dream. When they opened, flight attendants were picking up cups, and passengers chatted in the distance. It wasn't a nightmare, but a blustery wicked storm, swirling life and everything we had known to be normal out of control.

The term "failure to thrive" came more than once from the nurses who attended to her at the hospital where we fought to discharge her. Already hardened by previous misinformation, my husband Larry and I were not sure what to think of this latest assumption. Our hope was that the hospital in Rochester would be able to help our daughter, but it would be a while before arriving there. Once on the ground, there was still a two hour drive to make. Looking at my watch, I realized we'd be lucky to make it to admitting by midnight.

Christina moved her head and cried softly. I realized her ears were feeling the pressure change as the plane began to descend. Touching her cheek, I whispered softly, "It will be okay." Feeling a contradiction in my own words, I knew how serious her condition was and that we didn't know why she was ill, or how to help her.

The skies remained clear as millions of stars traded places with the lights of the Minneapolis-St. Paul area. As we descended, streets and highways became visible, illuminated by lighting. Looking similar to a miniature racetrack, vehicles moved in different directions.

When the flight attendant came by to check our seatbelts, she offered words of encouragement, citing Mayo as the best place in the country.

"They know what they are doing there. We wish you and your daughter the best of luck," she said empathetically.

A feeling of urgency came over me, for it wasn't luck that was needed. In fact, it was the farthest thing from Christina's need. For a moment I hesitated, almost afraid of what the reaction might be, until I could contain it no more.

"Don't forget to think of her when you pray," came rolling out, announcing the hope that was burning, dimmed by a tempestuous wind, but still lit.

What we needed for our Christina was a miracle.

One thing was certain we were in the fight of our lives, for her life. With this, just one of the squalls, of a violent storm with the worst yet to come. It would be the storm that would bring us to our knees in desperation and jubilation.

*Grandma and Grandpa holding Christina
in their new apartment.*

Chapter One
Our Perfect "Ten"

"Did I ever tell you about the oysters? Think about all the millions of oysters, just lyin' around at the bottom of the ocean. Then one day, God comes along. He sees one, and he says, 'I think I'm gonna make that one different.' He puts a little piece of sand in it, and it can do what all the other oysters can't. That one can make a beautiful pearl." —Fried Green Tomatoes

IT WAS A STORMY MINNESOTA Monday. Thick black clouds were rolling in when
Christina took her first breath.

With hands anchored on both sides of my enormous abdomen, I braced for the next painful contraction. It was hard to the touch. My mother's anxious voice pleaded with me, "The baby's not going to wait!" begging me to leave for the hospital. I couldn't imagine delivering our daughter without my husband. I refused to leave, hopeful the contractions would remain several minutes apart.

Inside the terminal the heavy late June air poured in. Knots of travelers hurried in all directions coming out of nowhere. Mathew, our toddler, reached his arms up in the air and with one scoop of her arm my sister Mary placed him on her hip. His little lips turned upward in a joyful grin. Now high enough to see, his flaxen blond head moved right then left as he observed hurried travelers passing through the gate, fresh off their plane.

Larry's plane had already been delayed by two hours, making the wait long and grueling without a chair to sit in. Leaning up against the wall for support, labor became painfully obvious. People passed by, some taking long glances in my direction. My cheeks flushed and were hot to the touch, undoubtedly from embarrassment mixed with intermittent pain and warm humid air.

Four months earlier Larry had accepted a lucrative job offer from a company in Texas. The contract required him to report for work within thirty days. Not wanting to move until our second child was delivered by our own doctor, Mathew and I remained in Minnesota while Larry flew back and forth on the weekends until our baby was due. He was supposed to be flying in days before she was to be born. Little did he know that he would be arriving just in time…maybe!

Intermittent voices echoed from the speakers, announcing departures and arrivals, when at last Larry's flight number was heard. Former passengers began flooding through the gate as I scanned them for my husband. Night had fallen and the terminal was dimmer than before. At last the tall strong familiar silhouette emerged from the crowd of people.

"Daddy!" shrieked Mathew as he jumped down and dove for his father. With outstretched arms Larry caught him in mid-air. Holding Mathew in one arm, he kissed me and gazed into my eyes for a moment. "Are you okay?"

The touch of his hand sent waves of relief through me. "I'm glad you made it." Still waiting for his answer, he looked down at my hands and his eyes widened when he realized I was in labor. Taking my hand while holding Mathew with the other arm, Larry led as we wove through the crowd and headed out the door. Mom's face softened as she wiped tears of relief that Larry had made it home in time. We arranged to meet her and my sister later at the hospital.

I sighed as we drove. "I did not want to deliver our daughter without you."

Labor had progressed and by the time I was in a room my water broke. An epidural was placed to ease the pain. When numbness traveled into my chest and labor slowed to a crawl, we knew something was wrong. Larry rushed to the nurses' station and a doctor and nurse raced back. The medication in the epidural was overdosed—the epidural stopped.

"This shouldn't have happened," Larry said sternly. He was already tired from the trip and exhaustion was setting in as the hours ticked away into early morning.

Larry's deep voice came in through the intense pain of the contractions.

"You can do it. Push and hold it, honey."

Pushing wasn't working and endless exhaustion set in. Pain throbbed in my lower back. When the door burst open and my doctor rushed in, Larry smiled, thankful he had arrived. Minutes earlier the nurse told us the baby wasn't advancing with contractions and her heart rate had elevated. After my doctor assessed the situation an intense rush began. Placing his hand on our baby's head to guide her out, he instructed me to take a deep breath and push. Both the doctor and nurse kept glancing at the window during the birth as the darkness rolled in. It was one of those intense, blackening, early morning storms that seldom happened.

Thunder cracked and lightning flashed with one last push and our beautiful baby girl was born. Holding her head in one hand and her bottom with the other, Larry carefully scanned each tiny finger and toe. Our "pearl" had arrived. Her soft cry mixed with relief filled voices as the doctor and nurses went through their post-birth procedures.

"A healthy seven pounds, five ounces," announced a grinning doctor.

Larry moved his head close to mine, tears rimming his tired blue eyes as he whispered, "She's perfect."

Christina scored a perfect "ten" on the Apgar (new born evaluation score) extinguishing concerns from the epidural mishap and the upsetting lab results early in the pregnancy. During the first trimester, abnormal results indicated a possible genetic disorder. A level III ultrasound and amniocentesis were done, which ruled this out. Even so, we worried through the rest of the pregnancy.

"Why, Larry, I think she looks like you!" the nurse exclaimed. There was no doubt she was his daughter, the ovate eyes, the roundness of his head, the same. Her hair, however, was medium brown, the same as mine. I wondered if it would remain that way. Minutes after her birth, rays of sunlight began peeking through clouds, which were dissipating as quickly as they had come.

Baby book entry: June 28, 1997

Christina, your father said he is glad you are healthy. He worried about you ever since the first test was done. Relief showed on his face! You are perfect.

"Go on, it's okay." Larry urged Mathew on. He slowly walked toward the bed. His little emerald blue eyes twinkled with curiosity as if to say, "This is no doll." Bending over Christina, he gently kissed his new baby sister. At that moment I knew dreams do come true. For years Larry and I had prayed for children. Even after surgery to repair my only fallopian tube, the doctor had given less than a twenty-five percent chance that we could have children of our own. Still, we continued steadfast each night in our plea. With Mathew born twenty-one months earlier and now Christina, we were twice blessed. My heart was full, our family complete and with the upcoming move, life was exciting. It could not get any better.

Laying Christina on my chest, I hugged her gently and realized after already giving birth to Mathew, I felt more confident. I'd done this before. The fears that hovered were gone. It was smooth from here on out; or so I thought.

A cloud of dust swirled over the driveway as the moving van packed with our furniture and belongings rolled away. It felt strange to watch it disappear from sight. Waiting in the car for Larry as he made one last round through the house, I thought back to our last visit with my grandparents. Grandpa hummed as four week old Christina lay sleeping on his lap. He loved this. When my ten brothers and sisters and I were young, he would hum, sing and play the accordion for us. Standing on a stool in her kitchen, Grandma directed as I put her freshly washed goblets away in the position she wanted them. Even in her nineties, there was an order to her home that flowed with calmness because she was such a masterful housekeeper. It wasn't going to be easy moving away from them. Larry and I adored them and worried their fragile health could take a turn for the worse. Mathew clung onto Grandpa's leg as we said our goodbyes. Holding Christina, Grandma kissed her over and over.

"Grandma, we will see you again, soon," I said in an effort to comfort her—dismissing any thought we wouldn't.

After our first stop, only thirty minutes from the home we had just left, a wind of uncertainty swept through me. Anxious thoughts began thundering through my mind. From out of nowhere and certainly not the best timing I turned to Larry. "What if God doesn't want us to move?"

He gave me a "you're out of your mind" kind of look.

"I don't think we should be doing this," I said, shocked at my own words. I didn't move.

"Honey, we have an apartment waiting for us in Texas. Not to mention the moving van left with all of our things on it."

He turned the key in the ignition. Silence. He tried again. Silence. With a confused look, he got out of the car and opened the hood. After a few minutes of investigation he slammed it down.

"What timing! The starter must have gone out!"

Little did we know that car problems would be the least of our worries a few months down the road as a different kind of storm would be rumbling.

Mathew, Whitney, and Mom holding Christina
in front of our soon to be new home.

Chapter Two
The Front of the Storm

"The kind of faith God values seems to develop best when everything fuzzes over, when God stays silent, when the fog rolls in." -Philip Yancey

THE SPLASH DRIFTED THROUGH THE air similar to a dollop of butter dropping into a pan of deep liquid. A rush of adrenaline took over and I leaped from the lawn chair causing it to skitter backward scraping the burning concrete. The splash had come from the adult pool, farther away. With one foot dripping with water from the wading pool it had been in, I darted for the adult pool.

"Mathew!" I called out, scanning the water for my son. His blond hair floating wildly as he sank toward the bottom. I dived in. My fingers caught an arm. Wrapping my hand around it, I pulled him toward me. When my feet hit the pool bottom, with a shove, by will as much as force I propelled him toward the surface. Swimming up, with my hands on his swim diaper, I pushed him onto the concrete edge of the pool.

"Mathew" I screamed. "Breathe!"

Water spewed from his mouth and nose as he tried to gasp for air with a terrified look on his face. He began sputtering and spitting until he coughed deeply, almost throwing up. With a tint of blue to his lips Mathew shivered and began wailing, "Mommy!" His arms were wet and dripping as he clung to me.

"Matt, are you okay?" Tears slid down our wet faces as I held him tightly in my arms. "What were you thinking? I told you to stay by mommy." Feeling shaky and weak, the legs holding me up wanted to collapse. Still holding Mathew, I reached the lawn chair I had just come from and lowered the two of us onto it. Christina was unmoved by the near tragic event, remaining quiet and somewhat asleep in her covered carrier. Feelings of relief began to seep through me, then guilt. *This wasn't his fault—I should have kept my eyes open and on him.* Relaxing with my eyes closed from the sleepy heat, and one foot submerged in the blue water to feel the waves as Mathew played was not enough.

To beat the sizzling Texas heat, the kids and I visited the pool area early in the day. Without knowing my way around while Larry worked, this was a break from the tedium in our temporary apartment. Shortly before Christina's morning nap, we headed for the pool area, usually vacant since many renters were at work or in school. While she slept in her carrier next to me, Mathew splashed in the wading pool adjacent to the adult pool, deep enough for serious divers. The adult pool was separated from the wading pool by a stone walkway a few feet wide. Upon hearing that "deep" more distant splash, it was like waking suddenly from a dream. Still breathing heavily, I looked around and up at the apartment balconies encircling the pool area. *Did anyone even see what happened?*

Shifting Mathew to face me, I sternly commanded, "This is the only pool you can go in," my finger pointing to the wading pool. Then pointing directly at the adult pool, I said, "No!"

As if on cue, little Christina began to fuss. Turning my back on Matt long enough to pick her up, Mathew bounced from the chair. Without any reservation, already recovered from the scare, my fearless son, jumped into the wading pool and began splashing. His eyes focused right at me as if to say, "Is this okay?" He knew it wasn't.

"Mathew, come on. Mommy is done with the water for to-day—come here."

He made no effort to get out. As he splashed closer to the adult pool, I stepped forward, Christina cuddled in one arm, as I stretched the other arm out to grab him. Before I could he lunged into the water keeping his head above while kicking his legs. Water splattered both Christina and me.

"Can I help you?" inquired a slender blonde woman standing by the pool. Her words lingered over the vowel sounds.

A touch of embarrassment flashed through my cheeks. *Did she see what happened?* "No, I'm okay, I think." Locking onto Mathew's hand, he half-walked and half-splashed his way back to the safety of the lawn chair with me.

She didn't leave, but remained there holding mail in her hand, "I was just pickin' up the mail when I saw you—I'm Shelley. Sure you don't need any help?" she asked again stooping to pick up a towel that had fallen. "Whitney, my eleven-year old knows who you are. She told me someone new moved in with two youngin's, I think you fit that description." It wasn't long before we were friends and Shelley's daughter started coming to visit almost every day.

At three months old Christina tried to hold her head up for long periods while lying on her stomach. "Christina, wook at mommy," Mathew urged, sitting close to her with one arm over her back. He smiled at the camera while Christina had an ador-ably curious look on her face. I focused the lens quickly to take the shot. With her eyes fixed at the camera I pressed the shutter button. Still looking through the lens I watched as her right eye crossed in toward her nose. Lowering the camera, I examined her face. An odd look shadowed her face, and she suddenly threw up.

"What was that?" I said out loud.

Mathew looked at her curiously. "Mommy, she's sick." he said, wrinkling his nose.

Worried and confused, I turned to Larry. Before saying anything he responded,

"Paulette, I'm sure she is fine—maybe she's not feeling well." Then jokingly he mused, "At least we know she didn't jump into a pool."

"Very funny." It was amusing but only for a moment. "Still," I reminded him, "those feelings, they aren't going away." Wanting nothing more than me to feel better he kissed my forehead. "It is going to be fine."

With each day, Christina became fussier and at times inconsolable. Falling asleep for her was only a taunt. Soon afterward she would wake crying seemingly in distress. Her back would arch, and I would wonder if she was trying to push away from being touched or held. The arching transformed into scrunches and her little body would flex—pushing her legs straight.

"She seems in pain. Something is wrong," I explained to the pediatrician.

It had to be gas. That's what I wanted the doctor to tell me at the local pediatrician's office. Instead, he diagnosed her with reflux, a condition where the esophagus would burn due to not closing properly.

"This is very common at this age." Sure of his diagnosis the pediatrician stated, "Babies usually grow out of this by the time they are six or seven months old."

During the next three months we rushed our daughter into the clinic ten times. Overwhelmed and concerned with her constant crying, we begged for answers. With the exception of ear infections, nothing was found that would cause her any discomfort.

The young receptionist rolled her eyes. "Here she comes again. What it is this time?" she whispered to another receptionist, loud enough for me to hear. Turning to each other, they giggled on my behalf. Insecure already, I began questioning myself. *Am I capable of caring for my child? Are these feelings just nerves—my nerves?*

Less than confident, I again explained her symptoms to the doctor. "She constantly spits up no matter how much or how little she eats, and sometimes in the middle of the night she will wake for no reason and begin to throw up." The same diagnosis was heard from different pediatricians from the same office.

"She will grow out of this," one physician said. "They always do." Then he began to tell me the story of his child, who had reflux: "… and by the time she was six months old, it was over."

It was crystal clear, the doctors at this clinic, weren't taking me seriously.

Neon lights hung on the wood walls above long wooden tables. Wide windows aligned the outer walls with only a screen separating the outdoors.

"Mathew, come dance with me!" Whitney yelled. As he walked toward her he was sidetracked by a man standing on top of a wooden table in the middle of the room. A thin rope wrapped around the back of the tall young man's neck and attached to a washboard that hung over his chest. He strummed it in a guitar-like manner with both hands. Mathew slowly walked toward Whitney, not taking his eyes off the interesting musician.

Putting his arms up to Whitney she took them and they began to twirl like disco dancers to a country tune. Mathew stopped long enough to clap along as if he knew the melody like an old familiar tune. His head bopped up and down while he twirled on the wooden dance floor like a whirlwind. They were having the time of their lives. The oldest dance hall in Texas, Gruene Hall, stood five minutes from our home. The historic dance hall was surrounded by rows of buildings filled with things for sale, like handmade crafts, Texas souvenirs and homemade ice cream. During the day and night in Gruene Hall, musicians would play for tourists and locals alike. Pictures of prominent country stars who had played here spread over one hundred years of history filled spaces on the walls. This was as Texas as anything could be.

Christina was restless on my lap, when she flinched the first time. Holding a cloth to her mouth in case her stomach was upset, I felt her flinch again. Then she scrunched forward and began to cry. Her face, seconds before angelic in sleep, was now grimaced as if in pain. Her legs flexed and she held them there, gurgling and crying. I prayed for it to stop, hopeful no one saw. When it didn't stop, I called for Mathew and Whitney.

"We have to leave. It's happening again."

I fumbled in my purse for my cell phone. "She needs to see the doctor, right away!" I pleaded into the phone. Grudgingly, the receptionist said to bring her in. Christina began pulling her knees up toward her chest. She became still and unmovable, crying, wincing and choking often.

"Something has to be done!" I pleaded with the doctor to investigate further. Reluctantly, he agreed to run further tests. A catheter was inserted to check for signs of a urinary or kidney infection and blood taken. After the initial results came back negative for any kind of infection, the doctor sucked in air and blew it out rather obviously and moved close to me. "Everything is normal—perhaps sleep might help." He looked sternly at me. "Not for her, but for you."

His arm slid around my shoulders as if to comfort me. It felt uncomfortable and the room seemed to fill with heaviness. I wanted to move but didn't. "Are you getting enough rest?" The implication of his words began to register and sting as he proceeded to explain the effects of post partum depression. He was implying, *I was the problem*.

My shoulders lowered, and I slid from under his arm. Anger brewed as redness climbed up my neck and my cheeks became hot. Did he really think I would want my baby to endure pain for no reason? What did he think of me? I walked over to the examining table, slid one hand under my daughter and gently picked her up. Extending one hand to Mathew, he obediently put his little hand in mine and gazed at me with a serious look. No sound was uttered. Warm tears of frustration rolled down my face as I walked angry but silently out of the clinic.

A bladder infection would just have been too simple. We could give her medication, and then she would be better. Not being able to help our daughter was haunting me. Why didn't I feel better after being told nothing was wrong with her? The foreboding feelings that were present before we had left Minnesota still lingered in the background of my soul like a heavy weight. It was almost as if I was unconsciously waiting for clouds to become visible that would reveal a storm front moving in, with damaging winds hidden just behind the beauty of it.

Upset at the events of the day, Larry left the office early to come home, worried about his daughter. Pacing back and forth in the apartment, he fought the same anger I had felt at the clinic. His face showed the fastidious thoughts he was having. Light brown hair filtered through his fingers as his hand slowly moved across his head while he weighed what we should do next. He, too, believed something was wrong with our daughter; but what? It all seemed foggy, as if we couldn't see something right before our own eyes.

"It's time to take your doctor's advice," he decided and immediately began flipping through the yellow pages. The instruction from my doctor who delivered Christina was lodged in my memory: "Go to a clinic or hospital in a large city." Adamant to find the right help, Larry began circling pediatricians in San Antonio, forty-five minutes away, the closest large city.

A phone call brought the news that grandma was in the hospital. She had fallen and broken her hip. Surgery was needed. She never recovered from the surgery. A veil of pain and guilt consumed me absorbing the news of her death. I worried for my grandfather. After sixty years of marriage, would he survive alone? Here we were living life in Texas. Were we doing the right thing by being here? Emptiness filled my heart realizing I could no longer pick up the phone and call her—which out of habit, I did more than once in the days to come. An accumulation of disappointing thoughts became friends with the already unsettling feelings that we harbored.

"Could there be any more uncertainty?" I cried to Larry, "Between losing Grandma, the worries about Christina's health and Mathew a busy two-year-old, I feel overwhelmed." Wrapping his arms around me, we stood there for a moment and we prayed together. His comfort during my pain was the binding that kept me from falling apart.

Rosebushes given to us by my mother when each child was born were planted in the brick flower box aligning the front of our new home. Walking up the sidewalk, the smell of the recently planted flowers intoxicated the surrounding air.

The builder's representative and our new neighbor, Sharon, stopped by to make sure everything was in order in our new home. Dishes and pans were strung across the tile counter tops. Open boxes sat on the tile floor of the kitchen. On the only open area of carpet in the living room, Christina lay on her blanket. While Mathew napped in his room, Sharon watched as Christina began to push up with her arms and locked her legs.

Knowing our concerns surrounding her development Sharon exclaimed, "She is trying to crawl, Paulette!" For that moment, my sadness and concerns melted at the sight of Christina's achievement. A simple milestone made. Accompanying this achievement were coos and gurgles. Our Christina was determined.

"This isn't kitchen supplies," I said unpacking an infant jumping seat. Remembering how Mathew loved jumping in this, I eagerly hung it in the doorway. Placing Christina securely in the seat we waited. "There you go, honey. Move your legs." Nothing happened. Christina's legs dangled lifelessly under her. Taking her legs gently in an attempt to help her jump, I lifted her up a few inches and down again. She didn't move on her own. Not an inch or even a jiggle.

"Maybe she's not ready," Sharon softly explained.

The cloud of worry about her development came back and hovered over to the appointment with the new pediatrician.

"Some kids like it, and get the hang of it, while others just don't," the doctor explained. "Nothing to worry about." Was I just worrying too much? After all, I was no expert at being a parent. After the doctor finished examining her, he checked her development. A reassurance came when he went over the results with me. She was on track developmentally and seemed healthy.

"However, I think at this point we need to address the reflux. I'd like her to see a gastroenterologist." The new doctor seemed to be proactive. Finally, something was being done to help Christina's constant throwing up.

"Her six-month immunizations are due soon," the doctor reminded. "She should probably have them."

"I know she is due, but Larry and I want to wait. She is still throwing up and until the tensing up is better, we'd like to wait," I replied, hopeful for agreement.

When he concurred with me, I was reassured we were doing the right thing by seeking another opinion in San Antonio. Within days the gastroenterologist prescribed medication to help soothe Christina's stomach upset. It seemed a success when the dogged vomiting lessened.

Although temporary, it brought a welcome breeze of calmness to our new home.

*"God will use pivotal circumstances in our lives, to do something **in** us not **to** us."* —*Pastor David Nelson*

"We don't want you in the dark, friends, about how hard it is when all this came down on us in -[the hospital] Asia Province. It was so bad we didn't think we were going to make it. We felt like we had been sent to death row, that it was all over for us.....instead of trusting on our own strength and wits to get out of it, we were forced to trust God totally--not a bad idea since he's the God who raises the dead." 2 *Corinthians 1:9-8 (NIV)*

Chapter Three
The Torrential Storm

God moves in mysterious way His wonders to perform; He plants his footsteps
on the sea and rides upon the storm.—William Cowper

BOUNCING AROUND THE HOUSE WITH excitement,
Mathew ran toward the entryway hearing the chime of the
doorbell. Friends from Minnesota had arrived, Roger and Terri with their daughter Miranda. It wasn't long before Mathew
and Miranda ran through the house playing. When one giggled,
the other giggled. When Mathew put on sunglasses, Miranda
found a pair and did the same. With pacifiers in their mouths
and sunglasses perched on their noses, they posed as rock stars
for the camera.

The house filled with laughter and happiness while reminisc-
ing with our friends. All of us laughed recalling the time I threw
a softball on a bet, breaking the windshield of Larry's truck. Larry
and Roger talked about Larry's new job and the softball team
both of them had played on for years. Christina still fussed a lot,
but with the exception of lingering rosy cheeks from her recent
immunizations three days earlier, things seemed better. Along
with a fever, she cried after the shots, making a strange screeching
sound. The nurse reassured me this was all normal, even listening
to her cry over the phone. With her cheeks still flushed, Larry and

I wondered if we should call the doctor's office again. Before we had the opportunity, things took a dramatic turn.

"Larry, what just happened?" I said frantically.

"Nothing, she was just dozing off to sleep." The look on his face showed uncertainty.

Christina's little head began to drop down then it suddenly came up again. Tears streamed down her face while at the same time she was smiling.

"Larry, what's wrong with her?"

"Honey, I am sure she is just very tired."

In my arms while holding her, the strange behavior stopped. She must have been exhausted, I rationalized. Her eyes closed and together we fell asleep.

Aroma of coffee brewing filled the early morning air as Larry left for the office. On cue Christina woke and Mathew came running to the kitchen excited to have company in our home. Still in her pajamas, I lowered Christina into her walker and kneeled in front of her, examining her face.

"Mommy loves you, are you...?

Her head dropped and a moment later it came up, she was smiling and tears dripped down her cheeks. *Does she see me?* Her eyes seemed to be looking at me, but it didn't seem as though she saw anything.

Terri set her cup down and looked at Christina, surprised.

"I have to take her in to the doctor. Something isn't right. Sorry about this. I know we had plans to do some sightseeing today."

Lifting Christina out of the walker, I pulled her close, putting my hand on the back of her head and gently holding her. She began to scrunch her body forward in my arms.

The secretary at the pediatrician's office told me there were no appointments available until later that afternoon. After explaining the situation she put me on hold. When she came back she said, "The doctor will be waiting."

Fear of what this might be consumed me for the forty-five minute drive to the pediatrician's office.

"She looks fine. No temperature and her heart rate normal," he stated. "Look, she is even smiling!"

"I know," I said. "Right now, she is fine. But she was not fine last night or this morning. Please, we have to do something."

"All right. I can send you over to a neurologist and have an EEG done. If nothing else, it will just reassure us that this is nothing to worry about."

The clipping of needles buzzing across paper to make their imprint was the only sound in the room. Christina had a cap on her head that fed electrodes through to her scalp. Her head was not dropping. Any hint of reassurance, however, was not coming from the face of the technician.

"Do you see something?" I queried.

He looked intently at the lines being drawn, and then he glanced at Christina with an intense searching look. "The doctor will explain. Please wait for him." His voice was quiet, and it seemed he didn't want to discuss this with me.

I pulled her closer and began to wish we were somewhere else. I prayed silently that she would be okay.

Before explaining anything the neurologist peppered me with questions.

"Do you have any family members on either side that have delays developmentally? Are there any genetic disorders in your family? Does Christina have any birthmarks?" He started turning the pages of the EEG readings. He Pointed to lines on the pages as if I knew what they meant. Responding to his questions, I tried to remain stoic, but it didn't last long. My heart thumped inside my chest and tears slipped down to my chin.

"Every eight to ten seconds her brain is seizing." He spoke calmly and to the point. His tall thin frame towered over me as he emotionlessly explained Christina's condition. "This is called 'status epilepticus.'"

"What does that mean?" I cross-examined.

His voice lowered to a steady serious tone as he told me, "It means her brain is seizing constantly. She is in need of medical intervention. I need to admit her right now to the hospital." Before waiting for any comment he continued his interrogation, "Before today, what was going on with Christina? Has she seen a doctor recently?"

"Yes, she was seen several times for tensing up and throwing up. Both my husband and I had been concerned about it. Just a couple of days ago she was given a set of immunizations…" stopping suddenly my mind raced backward to the last doctor visit. Clean bill of health, less throwing up. Immunizations were given, five at one time. Inhaling a deep shaky breath, fear gripped at the remembrance of news programs accusing immunizations of causing serious injury to children.

"Did the immunizations cause this to happen?"

"I don't know at this point. Tell me what the doctors said about her spitting up?" he asked. "Did they ever advise you to have an EEG done?"

I was confused. "Why would she need an EEG for spitting up?"

His reply came like a sharp open handed slap.

"Increased vomiting can be a sign that something neurological is happening," he explained. "The stomach produces more acid when a person has a seizure. Many seizure patients will throw up during one or after one."

Those menacing stormy feelings I had were now confirmed. "Were these motherly instincts or the gentle nudge of the Holy Spirit?" Either way it was clear to me. "I had failed her."

Still in the room with the doctor I dialed the number to Larry's office.

"They are seizures," I told him. "She is having them every eight to ten seconds. She needs to be admitted to the hospital."

"What happened to her?" Larry's deep voice cracked and turned into a painful sound as though he was physically wounded. At his desk in front of several co-workers he began sobbing. My husband was noted to have a "tough guy" aura about him. It was never easy for him to let down his guard of any kind. This was deeply painful for him.

"Can you come to the hospital? We need you here?"

"I'm on my way."

The hallway to admitting seemed like a tunnel with people in a blur passing by us. I didn't want anyone to look at me, and I didn't want to look at them. This was painful. Did I miss something? Was she having seizures before this? Did I keep her from the proper medical care? The day she was born she scored a perfect ten. She seemed so healthy then.

As she was being admitted, Christina dropped forward every few minutes. I knew now these were seizures. Her stomach was constantly upset. A blanket became too soiled, so I threw it in the trash. The doctor's words kept repeating in my head. "Every eight to ten seconds, she is having seizures."

Christina's soft spot on the top of her head was still evident as the indents marked where the electrodes were attached. Her blue eyes, resembling the almond shape of Larry's, were exhausted but not yielding to rest. Her outfit now stained from multiple episodes of sickness, looked a mess. I wanted nothing more than to run a warm tub and bathe her, rubbing the sweet smell of baby oil on her. Instead, we waited for a sterile hospital room to open.

Why did he want to know if she had any birthmarks? Why didn't I ask him this? What else was I forgetting to ask him? Was she having seizures before? I felt like screaming. The tensing up, was that seizure activity? The thought that she was in trouble and didn't know it made me nauseated.

It seemed several hours passed but it was only one when Larry came around the corner. "Hey," he said quietly, anguish etched on his face. Taking Christina he cuddled her and kissed her.

"Thank God, you're here!" Both of us felt broken as we huddled together, comforting one another. That day I fully understood the intention of a special verse in scripture: *Bear one another's burdens, and so fulfill the law of Christ.* (Galatians 6:2 ESV.) To bear one another's burdens is the supreme imitation of Jesus. We imitate Jesus, the ultimate burden-bearer.

We took hands with our daughter in our arms, and together prayed. "Lord, please be with us right now. This is overwhelming, and we don't know what to do. Keep Christina safe. Please heal her."

Could we have prevented this from happening? After the countless visits to the doctors—how could they have said it was normal reflux without checking into it further? We wondered what would have happened had we known the upset stomach was from seizure activity. Would we have allowed the immunizations?

We tried to remain strong as bolts of lightning-like fear flashed at the course entirely uncertain. When either of us attempted to understand how this could have happened, it blew us into torrential compunction and unleashed gripping emotion. Life as we had known it was swirling out of control. The storm had arrived.

Chapter Four
Warning Sirens

"Now sirens have a still more fatal weapon than their song, namely their silence...someone might have escaped from their singing; but from their silence, certainly never." –Franz Kafka

THE OFFICE WAS SILENT, EXCEPT for the distant rumble and clatter of traffic rushing up and down Highway 35W, which ran parallel to the building. The phones had not started ringing; it was too early. The large office—consisting of several desks aligned in a huge semi-circle with yellow and white forms that looked like piles of autumn leaves—was dwarfed by the warehouse below. The warehouse held hundreds of pallets of freight, much of which Larry was responsible for moving from Texas to other places across the country. A huge window allowed office personnel to observe forklifts scurrying between isles carrying and moving freight. Larry worked at this trucking brokerage office with Chet, who scrunched his forehead and pursed his lips while glaring at Larry. When he stood, his tall frame supported by expensive earth colored western boots carried a rotund belly slightly obscured his oval belt buckle. Chet glanced at the calendar on his desk, his black cowboy hat covering his eyes and wrapping his face in a shadow. His head snapped up, and he glared at Larry.

"Do you really need to be there? Your wife can handle this on her own." His voice was laced with a northern monotone. Even though he had lived in Texas for several years and looked the part, he spent most of his life until now in the northern part of the United States.

"I can't leave her alone. Paulette needs me there, and so does Christina. Tomorrow, I promise to come in early." Larry turned and walked back to his desk, not waiting for a response, knowing it wouldn't come. After checking messages he wrote notes for his assistant, then promised Chet he would check in regularly throughout the day. He left the office, heading for San Antonio before the clock struck seven a.m.

Guilt loomed, thickening the stale hospital room air. Larry and I took deep difficult breaths in an effort to rid ourselves of this oppression. We'd never witnessed a seizure before yesterday or realized we had seen one. Less than 24 hours later, we witnessed more than fifty seizures torture our daughter's little body. A parent's worst nightmare—not, this was worse.

Draped over a goose necked stainless steel tray, rested a small starch looking white garment resembling a small chef's coat. *What is this used for?* Larry's concerned gaze met mine, and we gave each other a silent shrug as if to say, "I don't have a clue."

Slipping the garment behind Christina, the nurse wrapped the material around her and secured it by joining the attached Velcro. Our daughter could not move with the exception of one arm being left out for them to use for the IV. This IV would be used for injecting dye into her veins to illuminate the images they would view. The name of this odd white material thing had evaded me until it was on our daughter—*straight jacket.*

I felt Larry's fingers wrap around my arm and pull me toward him, guiding me out of the way of two other nurses rushing in to place an IV. I couldn't help stifle the negative thoughts. *Is this really necessary? She is only seven months old. How hard would it be to hold one arm?* But I said nothing. She shrieked and cried when the needle went in and I found myself feeling irritated at them for hurting my daughter. This seemed backward. The doctors had been treating *us* like we were mad ones, wanting to blame this on post partum depression instead of listening to my pleas, and maternal instincts. They sent us home when they should have been treating my daughter. And now <u>she</u> was the one in the straight-jacket? It seemed unfair...I wanted the pain to stop.

Christina's little body relaxed when the medication began to take effect and her eyes closed and opened as she began falling in and out of sleep. Like most babies, she required a routine. Little did we know, walking down the hallway to the radiology department that day, that any kind of normalcy— including a schedule— would be out of the question for a profuse length of time.

We walked along as the bed with Christina rolled through the hallway until it came to a slow halt in front of two large double doors. A nurse with shoulder length brown hair told us that once they were ready to begin the test we would have to leave. It made us uncomfortable knowing we would have to leave her alone.

The room was quiet with the exception of humming from the huge MRI machine. Christina was placed on her back, near the opening of the MRI machine. Its metal and plastic surface shone slightly in the dim burning florescent light, and its circular mouth was threatening.

Both of the large metal doors abruptly burst open, startling Larry and me. A tall thin man swiftly walked in, draped in a white jacket with a stethoscope dangling from his neck. He strode past without acknowledging us and went to Christina. He did not speak a word nor did he glance in our direction. This silent medical person examined our daughter, checked her pulse and then injected something into her IV.

It was as if we were in a frozen state, just watching an event taking place without being a participant. *How strange! Is this the radiologist? If so, did he not see us, the parents, standing right here?* The curious focused stare of Larry's eyes caused me to follow where they were fixed—on our daughter's face. With web of IV tubing and electrode cords attached to her, she was given a medication to calm her before we left the room to calm her, but something was odd. She was still, not a hint of even a pulse, her eyes strangely wide open and staring at the ceiling. Looking up there was nothing on the ceiling other than tile. I wondered what it was that caught her attention. Her expression was strange—almost as though she was looking, but didn't actually see anything. Her eyelids didn't blink, but remained fixed—we became frightened and wanted to know what was happening. Her face was lifeless, and I realized she wasn't asleep nor was she consciously aware of her surroundings. I feared her odd countenance and stare was a reaction to the chemical the man had just administered into the IV. Both Larry and I watched her intently, when, all of the sudden, a loud noise which caused us both to flinch exploded amidst the silence of the room.

"Bam—Bam—Bam!" The fist of the man standing next to Christina pounded hard, on the metal surrounding the opening of the machine—directly above Christina's head.

What is he doing? And then he did it again, "Bam—Bam—Bam!" Larry straightened up and took a step toward him.

"Hey," he began, but the man ignored him and bent forward as he slid the stethoscope from his neck and placed the cool diaphragm on Christina's chest. She did not flinch or move in response to the instrument touch her skin, or previously to the loud noise of his pounding.

Fear was absorbing me as my mind raced to understand what was going on.

"What is happening?" came out in little more than a whisper, but no one answered.

Finally Larry directed a question to the man in the white coat, "What was that you put in the IV?"

With his back still to us, he spoke for the first time, "I put medication into the IV that will put her to sleep."

"Is that what is making her stare?" Larry requested.

"No. The medication has not even had enough time to work yet," he replied stanchly. It was then he moved enough for us to read his name tag and learn he was the radiologist—a doctor. We *assumed* he was here to perform the MRI. Again, he knocked loudly, "Bam—Bam—Bam!" Christina did not flinch or move her eyes, still fixed on the ceiling.

Her body relaxed suddenly when the medication took hold, and her eyes closed. The doctor checked her breathing and pulse again, then waved to someone unseen behind a glass window. The machine slowly took her in.

Without saying a word or looking at either Larry or me, the doctor left the room. The nurse escorted us out and gave us directions to the recovery room where we would be able to see Christina in two hours.

My arm slid around Larry's for support. My legs seemed to drag as we stepped solemnly through the hallway. Slowing, almost stopping, more than once I had with a strong urge to run back into the room and pick her up. My head was light, and I couldn't think straight. *Why did she stare off like that and become so still.* And why, without saying anything, did they take her into the opening of the machine?

A handful of breakfast stragglers were finishing up meals and coffee, leaving the cafeteria nearly vacant by the time we had arrived. Sitting across from each other with trays of food in front of us, neither Larry nor I took a bite. Thoughts and fear held us captive and absorbed in our own bewilderment. After a long period of silence we began volleying questions: "Why didn't the unannounced radiologist tell us what was happening, or talk to us? What medicine/chemicals did he put into the IV—for that matter what were all the ones nurses had been putting in? Why so many and what side effects do they have? What should we be doing to help her?"

We deduced she had had a seizure while lying on the table, but why? She was given many doses of anti-seizure medications since she had been admitted the night before. If this was a seizure, it jolted us into the reality that we had no idea what seizures really were or if she would recover from them without permanent brain injury. We were clearly out of our league, suddenly thrust into the world of high-tech medicine, which to us was confusing and intimidating.

After what seemed like several hours, but was actually less than two, the recovery room nurse allowed us in to see our baby girl. The sight of her awake and moving about brought waves of grateful relief. Larry and I took turns holding her.

The nighttime hours seemed darker and drearier in the hospital. My mind raced mixing one thought with the next. *Will she be okay even though she is having seizures? Can a seizure cause brain damage, or was her brain already damaged? And, What is a metabolic disorder or genetic disorder?* All of these questions, with the exception of the last, brought the same answer: We don't know. The neurologist explained what a metabolic disorder was in simple terms, referring to it as affecting the chemistry of our body. Genetics came in somewhere. The range was from bad to worse and manageable, in some cases. He reminded us, "Wait for the results of the MRI before we go on."

My wet eyes blurred the sight of Christina's beautiful baby face resting with intermittent sucks on her pacifier. Feeling desperate I began to pray, "Lord, help. I don't know what to do." I prayed for the MRI result to be normal. I loved her and her brother more than anything and thanked God for them. Admitting my helplessness, I begged for guidance.

In between seizure episodes the night crawled by slowly—I could not quiet my thoughts enough to rest. Mathew was home alone with our friends and I wondered if he was alright without me there. Did Larry find Mathew's clothes and everything all right? Were Roger and Terri doing all right? What a vacation. What were they thinking?

Dawn brought with it normal MRI results, and much needed relief from gripping concern that Christina's brain was not formed properly. It wasn't clearly understood what it all meant, but fluid levels in our daughter's brain appeared normal, and there were no physical abnormalities. The neurologist explained that in many children, the cause of seizures is never found. They call these idiopathic. He explained that many children can outgrow seizures, whereas others are found to have genetic or metabolic disorders. Because of the intensity and frequency of our daughter's seizures, he was suspicious it was the latter.

"I am ordering another EEG to be done," the neurologist explained, "to see what kind of activity we are seeing today. Then we can go from there."

"Okay," I said happily absorbing the "normal" MRI result.

Other tests were ordered, including a 24-hour urine test where a catheter is placed and urine is collected for 24 hours, and blood work.

"Any seizures?" he asked.

Flashing back to the sleepless hours of the previous night filled with relentless seizures still fresh in my memory, I nodded yes. Each one was more frightening than the one before. Each time a slight rustle would sound, my heart would race. She would try to sit up, which at seven months old she still had not mastered, then her torso would scrunch forward at her waist. Her sleepy face turned red as she fell either to the side or forward onto her face. As quickly as possible my arms would wrap around her either to pull her up from falling or to grab her as she was falling. Many times she would throw up at the beginning or right after one—a stark reminder of the past. Her lifeless expression with each seizure changed into a stunned expression by the time it was over and she would come back. In an effort to comfort her I would hum, then sing until she fell back to sleep, which wasn't long after the seizure finished. For me, panic and fear wrestled with any attempt at sleep and was enhanced by exhaustion. Despair and anguish, already underlying my heart, came out as unstoppable sobbing let loose. Our daughter was lying in a hospital crib next to me, and I had no idea what to do to help her and no idea what the future for her would hold.

"Do you know what happened to her just before the MRI was done?" I asked the neurologist.

"Yes, the radiologist called me this morning. It's apparent to him she was having a seizure,"

Why didn't the radiologist say this to us? Twenty-four hours ago we saw our first seizure. When she was frozen on the table, we were out of our minds with fear at what was happening. Surely he saw how upset we were.

"That was frightening. I wish the doctor would have told us what was happening," I said in a lower-than-normal voice, almost as if I was afraid to make a statement. There was no reply from the doctor.

With the first major hurdle, the MRI result behind us, it was a happy, relief-filled moment, superseding the lack of communication and compassion from the MRI doctor.

Christina's medication was increased and another anti-seizure medication was added, which marked the beginning of a routine that would take place off and on during the next six months—in the hospital. An EEG machine came into the room being pushed by the technician who would be doing the test. The technician did his job then left telling me the doctor would be in to go over the results with me. Lab staff came in twice during the day to draw more blood, each time wrapping her in the straight-jacket. As soon as it was wrapped around her, she would begin to cry at being restrained, knowing that pain was to come. I wanted to trade places with her, if only I could. After three days in the hospital, the neurologist declared the EEG showed signs that medication might be working and, based on that, released Christina to go home with the condition that if the seizures changed or became longer, she must return immediately.

Baby book entry: February 5ᵗʰ – 7 months old
This afternoon we came home from the hospital…because you started having seizures. You have a lot of seizure activity in your brain. Many tears and hugs and kisses on you. Right now you are on anti-seizure medication…tonight you are in great spirits—even after all of the shots and pokes! We are praying, and so are many other people—we love you so much, Christina. You are going to be fine!

It was Roger and Terri's last day in Texas when we came home. The air, as Christina and I left the cool hospital, was hot, and I could feel the sweat sticking to my face. It never felt better. During our meal that night, we tried to have normal conversations—other than about the hospital or seizures. Miranda, clad in pink from head to toe, ran after Mathew, who was dressed in a Tiger outfit, as though nothing had happened. Their laughter was like music penetrating a dark dismal place. Mathew detoured from the chase long enough to throw his orange and black striped arms around me more than once—he was happy his mom was back home.

It was difficult to focus or to relinquish the thoughts and fears from the past few days. Being a good hostess was impossible. My emotions ran wild, from being thankful our friends were there to wanting no one to look at me. I forced myself to talk about other things that I had no real interest in.

Warning sirens had been screeching loudly and not taken seriously. It was as if we alerted the proper authorities, hailed a policeman wearing a white coat and notified him something was wrong, only for him to look up at the sky, feel the wind and see only clouds of calm in his view and declare nothing was wrong—it was we who were confused. Everything looked all right, therefore it was all right. But the sirens kept blaring, and somehow we became numbed by inaccuracy and rendered deaf. Worse yet, we gave in to something we felt was wrong. And now—and now Christina, our beautiful seven-month old, was paying the price. The consequence of not seeking shelter or making preparation to shield her from the turbulence of what could come was being paid.

Chapter Five
The Eight Letter Word: Epilepsy

"Times of great calamity and confusion have ever been productive of the greatest minds. The purest ore is produced from the hottest furnace, and the brightest thunderbolt is elicited from the darkest storm."—Charles Caleb Colton

———◆———

ONLY A FEW WISPY CLOUDS slipped across the pale-blue water sky above our Texas home. The warm air and tawny landscape reminded me more of autumn than winter—our friends were now driving back to frosted, sub-zero temperatures. Back in Minnesota we embraced the cold. Some even claimed to love winter, but today, feeling the warm "winter" air of Texas, I wondered why. The balmy weather, kindness and warmth in the culture was enchanting. The light of the dulled winter sun shone through the window and clung to Christina's skin as I finished securing the Velcro band on her diaper. She was clad only in a puffy white diaper, and I could see the brown and green bruises swathing large areas of her arms. On her head unnatural valleys formed from the electrodes. Two of them were red and prominent on her forehead. I stroked her fine hair with a gentle hand, tarrying on each indent in an attempt to massage it away. She lay still in her crib.

My attention briefly left Christina when I heard a voice calling from our front door. Mathew must have heard as well. The ever curious son, was already rushing for the front entry.

Upon seeing me, his trot turned into a sprint. I reached around him and swung the door open. Open armed Sharon lurched forward, wrapping me in a hug. Her daughter Amanda, five years older than Mathew, slid sideways between her mom and the door frame and took Mathew's hand. The two scrambled for his room. Stepping back, Sharon held her hands one on each of my shoulders, and smiled kindly right into my eyes.

"I want to see that darling baby!" Sharon exclaimed.

For a moment I felt as though no one should be here. I didn't want anyone to see this. It wasn't the way it should be. The word seizure alone terrified me, not to mention the stigma in my mind that came with it. *What would people think?* I'm ashamed, now, that such thoughts penetrated my mind—but in my defense this was frightening and seizures were awful and unfamiliar—we had never known anyone with them nor had seen anything like this. Hesitantly, I escorted Sharon to Christina's room.

Sharon's compassionate demeanor showed as the details of the hospitalization were summarized. She was not afraid of the diagnosis, she just wanted to be there for us.

"When I heard Christina was in the hospital, I couldn't believe it. You must have been very frightened, and look at her arms! Bless her heart." Her speech was warm and lilting. "If you need anything, anything at all, you promise to call me. I will be here, no matter what."

Her upset stomach returned and became a regular part of our day, unlike most families, the "healthy" days were unplanned and unexpected. We continued to pray that medications would control the seizures and that the long list of possible side effects, from a deadly rash to behavioral problems, would not affect our child. But when Christina would lie on a soft, cotton-blue blanket in the middle of the room and hardly move—I almost didn't recognize the motionless child as my own. Before the seizures, she was in constant motion, vigorous, having eyes that excitedly sparked and studied the world. Now, her eyes were dull. She made no effort to move herself. Her arms lay limply beside her head and lacked the strength—or interest—in lifting her torso as she had done before. Her legs were flat to the ground and didn't attempt to crawl. Christina would lift her head, at times, but it quickly dropped back to the softness of the blanket – I didn't know whether she was tired or had dropped from a seizure.

Dressed in his orange and black Tiger outfit, Mathew came running. "Bouncy, bouncy, bouncy!" he sang as he leaped from one area to the next. He loved reenacting the scene from the Winnie-the-Pooh poster above his bed where Tigger leaped across the poster, black curved lines depicted the bouncing course of his travel. It jarred my memory—previously Christina would coo or giggle, with her focus fixed on the colorful poster. Since coming home from the hospital, she had been quiet—no, actually she had not uttered a sound. I scooped her up and took her into Mathew's room, carefully positioning her to view the poster. Mathew, still in his tiger outfit, crawled up next to her. Solemn minutes ticked by until the only sound came from Mathew, who had barely been able to hold his quiet.

"Wook, Chistina! Wook-it!" Mathew's high pitched voice was urgent as he nudged her and motioned toward the poster.

Her head moved from side to side, not focusing on anything. Acting silly as could be, we motioned toward the poster with our hands, even whistling to gain her attention, but nothing we did enticed her to look at the poster that previously had enthralled her.

The sweet smell of baby shampoo filled our bathroom as I rinsed Mathew's hair. Stretching my arm to reach a towel, out of the corner of my eye Christina's head flopped forward toward the water. A plastic bathtub seat secured with suction cups to the tub floor kept her sitting, but it didn't stop her head from falling into the water. My palm shielded her face from hitting the water. The force of her head against my wet palm sounded like a clap, startling Mathew. Her face rested limply in my hand for a couple of seconds as I began to unclip the bar, then she regained consciousness and her innocent slightly red face looked surprised, as if to say, "What just happened?"

Before there was time to reach once more for the towel, it happened again and her head lay on the palm of my hand inches from the water. Mathew sat stiff without a sound, moving wide curious blue eyes back and forth between his sister and his mom.

"Larry, can you help me?" I called from the bathroom.

It didn't take but a second for him to be standing in the doorway and no explanation was needed as he witnessed the next seizure.

I worked quickly to maneuver her limp body out of the seat. I wrapped her in a towel snug to my chest and lowered us to the rocking chair in her room. Larry lifted an unusually quiet Mathew out of the tub, dried him and carried him to his room.

It was certain the seizures were getting worse. Terror now seemed like a resident in our house. In fact, it seemed to own it. She seized in my arms while wrapped in wet towels—scrunching forward then going limp. Just a few seconds would pass until her neck would straighten and a life giving breath would be inhaled and exhaled with a startled countenance. Like a thief in the night—another seizure neutralized any expression on her face. We didn't know what to do. *Should we call the doctor's office? Call an ambulance? Scream?*

Standing near the large wooden rocking chair, Larry watched intently while holding a telephone in his right hand. When he had seen enough, he dialed the doctor's office. His deep stalwart voice held back emotion as he urgently requested a call back from the doctor. Nearly twenty minutes passed and the "series" of seizures finally stopped. Finally, the phone rang.

Holding Christina up in front of me, I peered into her eyes listening to Larry's irritation-shaded voice. Looking at her directly for a couple of seconds, her eyes caught mine and she smiled. But her eyes blinked, closing our connection with the finality of a slamming door. When she opened them again, she was groggy. The connection was broken as the "post-ictal" (post-seizure fatigue) state began.

The doctor instructed us to admit Christina immediately. We began making arrangements. We did not want Mathew to witness the inevitable IV and the trauma of blood being drawn. It was nearly his bedtime, anyway. I remembered Sharon's kind offer to help us, but we couldn't reach her by phone.

When she didn't answer, I called the only other person in town we knew, L.A. (short for Lora Ann). She had helped us close on our home and was the wife of our builder. Thankfully, L. A. came without hesitation.

The asphalt freeway seemed almost invisible against what appeared to be the blackest of nights. Intermittent street lights illuminating the dismal journey back to the hospital in San Antonio.

Christina's tiny hands rested on the cushioned bar of her car seat and, with the exception of a few whimpers and dull cries, she remained quiet as we made our way through the night.

We signed in at the receptionist's desk of the hospital and settled into the cold waiting room's chairs for a long wait—even though they were expecting us. More than an hour passed while seizures tightened Christina's body then let go when she passed out, only to start over again every few minutes. Larry's face was creased with worry and his eyes sagged with weariness. He grew frustrated with the long wait and pleaded with the hospital staff until we were finally led to a room. The tall silhouette of the neurologist shone in the dim hallway as we neared the door to what would be Christina's her hospital room.

"How is she doing now?" Bending his head he gazed at Christina.

"About the same—they are coming often," Larry answered.

An brief EEG was done and the results handed to the neurologist, who gave us the dreaded results, "She is back to status. It's disappointing. We will be taking blood right away to make sure the medication level hasn't dropped. She will be given a medication that will put her to sleep for a long period."

Our world was tearing apart. The lucrative and seemingly "perfect" job was more demanding of Larry's time and energy than we'd imagined. The seizures were ill winds; they were harbingers of an ever-darkening storm. Neither Larry nor I had any insight into this illness—our limited knowledge made it impossible to know how to weather these troubles.

As the next 36 hours unfolded, we realized this hospital stay, riddled with questions, was not be as short as the first time. *What went wrong? Did something happen while I was pregnant to cause this?* Questions without answers were debilitating. Genetic and metabolic testing began, and, with that, several additional blood draws each day.

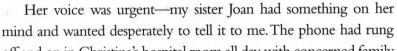

Her voice was urgent—my sister Joan had something on her mind and wanted desperately to tell it to me. The phone had rung off and on in Christina's hospital room all day with concerned family and friends realizing it had been more than a week since admission.

"A while ago, I watched this movie—about a boy with seizures. I know this sounds kind of weird, but I felt I was supposed to see this. Anyway, they put this child on a special diet and it stopped his seizures."

"What—? A diet for seizures?"

It seemed almost silly to think that a mere diet could be a treatment for this serious a medical condition. After all, wasn't medication the cutting edge of treatments? Her concern and suggestion was nice, but I held back an irritated tone as my sister continued.

"I wonder now if this might help Christina. Think about it. Who knows, it might help."

It was strange that she knew of a treatment the neurologist never mentioned. It had to be a fad and honestly, the thought of a diet sounded wonderful—too wonderful.

At nearly six o'clock p.m. I jarred the door open to hospital room and listened hoping to hear the patent sound of my husband's western boot clad footsteps. When they were heard, I peered out the door and down the hospital corridor. Whitney walked next to him holding Mathew's hand. Her cheeks and neck were flushed soft red, a sign that gave away she was nervous or upset. Eleven-year-old Whitney's time with us was usually fun, but this strange hospitalization was in contradiction to playing with Mathew or whirling him around on the dance floor at Greune Hall. I heard her sniffle as she approached the crib. Blue and pink animals—elephants and monkeys—twirled above Christina, but when she caught sight of Larry, she smiled and jerked her arms in a show of excitement. We all laughed. Mathew frowned at the tubing and began reaching for it in an attempt to move it away. I diverted him by picking him up. We rubbed noses and I tickled him.

"I missed you today!"

"I misses, you too."

Perhaps I read into his smile, but the happiness seemed to be shared with a sense of concern. Things were different. I worried for him. Was this strange or perhaps scary to him?

I gathered toiletries that Larry had brought and slung a towel and change of clothing over my arm. Hospital staff made it clear we were not allowed to leave Christina alone. Not that we would have ever do so—we knew how serious her condition was. But a warm shower and food had to wait for my husband's presence. As I began to exit the room, Larry voiced his disappointment. "Why can't a nurse come in and stay with Christina so you could take a shower or get something to eat?"

A new medication was added and, almost simultaneously, Christina seemed ill. She refused food and seemed to have an intestinal imbalance. Since the neurologist was out of the hospital for a couple of days, the nurse mediated conversation between us. I was confused why she had to mediate—I was clear that I needed to speak with him, yet he did not call.

The nurse repeated directions from the doctor, after her phone conversation with him. "He is convinced she is having a reaction to the newer medication. We are stopping it."

Even without the new medication, 48 hours later the symptoms became grave. Diaper changes needed to be done every half hour, and to me she looked ill. When the nurses' shift changed that evening, with still no word from the doctor, I took advantage of it and asked the new nurse to take a look. The evening nurse worked only a couple of days a week, but when she did, her positive smile and thorough examinations caused me to like her.

Bending over the side of the crib, she gently smoothed her hand over Christina's fine hair. She listened to her heart with the stethoscope and again ran her hand on the top of her head. Turning to me she looked over her glasses. A confused look was on her face.

"Her fontanel is sunken in. I don't understand how she could have gotten like this—she is very dehydrated. How long has this been going on?"

I recapped the last two days. "And I am still waiting to hear from the doctor."

She left to call the doctor.

I jarred the door just enough to let the hallway light leak in and heard muffled sniffle's while she spoke into the phone,

"No, Doctor, I don't know why—yes, I understand. Mom said she requested to talk to you. You will have to talk to the head nurse tomorrow."

Carefully conveying the doctor's message to me, she explained he never received my messages and was disturbed that his patient was dehydrated while under his care.

"None of my requests to speak with him were given to him?"

The nurse didn't look at me directly but I could tell she shed a few tears. "I guess not."

She explained that the neurologist had called in the gastroenterologist on an emergency basis.

"He should be here shortly."

It was painfully evident that we relied on the medical personnel here for more than they were able, willing and equipped to give. The only contact the nurses had with Christina were the ritual administration of medication through the IV. We changed her diaper. We held her. We comforted her. The nurses simply did not get near enough to know how she really was.

After the gastroenterologist examined Christina with rubber gloved hands, he ordered another IV to be placed. The current one she had been pulled out—and no one noticed until now.

It took an hour and many attempts from different staff members before the new IV was inserted and life giving fluids started flowing through her small veins.

Dozing on a lumpy hospital room recliner, my sleep steeped in agitation, the nurse woke me at three a.m. "Mrs. George? Test results are back. We need to move Christina."

While trying to focus, she explained Christina had a serious gastrointestinal virus. Since we were on the same floor as patients with cancer and cystic fibrosis, we had to move and reduce the risk of contagion.

I understood how dangerous sickness was to a child with a serious condition and would never want to endanger one. I wondered, however, how our daughter had contracted this? Mathew hadn't been sick, and Christina had been here in the hospital for almost a week.

It was a double edged sword. One level up, children had viruses and other contagious types of illnesses—ones we did not want Christina exposed to either, but what I didn't know was what waited for us on the floor above would turn my dread into profuse hope.

The nurse crept in silently, looking at the empty crib and then at me resting in the recliner. Snuggled under a blanket on my chest Christina sucked on a pacifier.

The dark haired nurse smiled when she saw us. "Well, hello there—I heard you two had a rough night."

Hearing the sound of her voice, Christina tried to sit up, more alert than anyone would expect. Her left arm was secured to a small cushioned board, assuring the IV would remain in place. She turned toward the nurse and smiled. For a moment I was taken back. It was not something expected after no food and such illness. The nurse concurred with my unspoken feelings.

"This is a welcome surprise!"

"It was a crazy night and few days for that matter, but look at her. I—I almost don't understand, she is so alert and happy."

With Christina, still on my lap, the nurse examined her.

"Any seizures recently?" That's when it dawned on me—she had not had one for a long while. *Is this my imagination?*

By evening when Larry arrived with Whitney and Mathew, Christina still had not had a seizure—even though she had not been able to keep food or medication down. Her inability to tolerate anything, including medication by mouth seemed curiously like a clue. It triggered the memory of my conversation with my sister. Larry and I sat across from one another and debated eagerly. Christina's nurse slipped into the room.

"Shouldn't she be having seizures without medication? Could a diet really help with seizures? If this is a treatment option, why didn't the doctor tell us?" We stopped and looked at the nurse. She was looking at us, too. I thought she had something to say, but didn't speak. I thought she might chastise us for thinking so bold, but she didn't and left the room.

Larry was stronger than me. He didn't care what she thought and wanted only to continue our conversation. Hours later, the same nurse returned, tiptoeing in.

She whispered, "I am not sure if it's okay to give this to you, so keep this between us, okay?" She handed me two pieces of paper and smiled a supportive smile, then left.

Being less than qualified in understanding medical jargon, I read the pages several times. With each word I read, an inner calm began to come over me with a feeling that this—this diet—could be the answer for our daughter.

"The value of fasting and the ketosis it produces as having a beneficial effect on seizure control has been recognized for centuries, and is recorded in two of the four gospels, The King James version, in Matthew 17:14-21 and Mark 9:14-29." The document went on to say, "Management of convulsive disorders by fasting and dehydration was observed and studied over a period of many years by leading Pediatric Neurologists of the time in leading Research Institutions, where it was noted that abstinence from food for a few days to several weeks resulted in temporary cessation of seizures, and improvement in the mental state in many patients with epilepsy, but the beneficial effects did not extend beyond the fasting period. Unfortunately, fasting could not be maintained indefinitely, and when re-fed, the seizures returned. These studies eventually led in 1921 to the formation of a ketogenic diet by Dr. R. M. Wilder, a diabetologist at Mayo Clinic, who at the time was trying to prolong the state of ketosis in diabetics. He suggested that the ketone bodies produced during starvation might be anti-convulsant, and he constructed a diet which would produce ketosis and at the same time furnish adequate food, by using the formula of an associate, Woodyalt, also a diabetologist. Because this diet causes a patient to remain in a constant state of ketosis, it later became known as 'the keto' or ketogenic diet." –THE KETOGENIC DIET INFORMATION SHEET, Author unknown.

It was as though we stumbled upon a secret that was kept our entire lives only 80 miles away from where we lived, but was now 1200 miles away. *Should we have moved? Could this be the answer we have been searching for?* When my sister told me about this diet, I was even put off by her suggestion. If there was a charge for being without knowledge and discrediting accurate sisterly intuition, I was guilty.

The doctor stood tall and straight, his voice firm and he shook his head from side to side. His words came out too straight forward or perhaps our hopes were too high, and this was desperately not what we wanted to hear.

"We can't risk it. The diet is not for children under one year—it could harm her."

After ruling out the ketogenic diet, Larry and I were not only disappointed, but without options. The only hope for seizure control relied on finding the right "mix" of medications.

Three weeks of hospitalization later it was difficult to have hope that anything would work. The neurologist flipped through her chart on the other side of the chest high counter of the nurses' station. I asked him what was next.

"Well, I think we need to wait for the blood and urine results to come in," he returned. "Maybe there will be the answer we are looking for. I can't release her like this. Even after she recovers from the virus, releasing her could put her in harm's way."

His words made me wonder if he was sure of a metabolic or genetic disorder. With my arms folded and resting on the ledge I peered over at Christina's chart, already thick with paperwork and saw, "Diagnosis: intractable *epilepsy*."

"Epilepsy—?" I exclaimed. "She doesn't have epilepsy—I don't understand."

Surprise and compassion glazed his face, "Mrs. George, Christina has epilepsy."

"I don't understand—what does intractable mean?"

"One seizure is a seizure, it could be from anything—a fever too high—but more than one is epilepsy. Intractable means…" He hesitated as though he didn't want to reveal what he knew would be a disappointing definition, "unstoppable."

Stepping back toward the safeness of the hospital room, I fought the urge to grab Christina and run. *Unstoppable seizures— I hate seizures—I hate epilepsy!* With all the medical miracles that modern science had created—we could replace a heart with metal and plastic, we had built machines to breathe for us, we could replace bones—why couldn't we cure seizures?

Begrudgingly, I pushed the door shut and broke into sobs. It wasn't only because I was frightened for her—no, it was more, so much more than that. It was as if we couldn't find the door that would open—it felt like being trapped, unable to outrun a tornado, or find the right key to unlock the secret. We were being blown about by the whims of hospitals and people in clean white jackets. Our lack of knowledge increased the surge when it came to medicine or even terms, like my new most hated word, *epilepsy*.

Christina, seven months old.
Three days before the first seizure

Mathew and Christina taken at his preschool two weeks later. Her
healthy baby face had changed since the onset of seizures.

Chapter Six
From Cinderblock to Watershed

"Like a lean stream swimming it way into a river, which seems a bit dangerous, but well worth the risk as it eventually feeds into an ocean full of miraculous beauty. It pales in comparison to anything else. All the trickles of water want to be there, but many dry up and lose their way. Others rush right into the strong river currents and have no trouble at all hearing the ever so quiet yet strong voice of the ocean they are drawn to. Some veer to the right and the left stumbling on rocks until finally, entwined in the river they eventually pour into the brilliant ocean." –Paulette George

RED AND PINK PAPER HEARTS mingled with angelic looking Cupid cut-outs brightening the dull beige of the hospital walls. Some were strung around the perimeter of the nurses' station. Clear-glass candy dishes contained jumbled pink and red and white heart candies, looking so sweet. The legend marking today of St. Valentine, allegedly passing a note from his jail cell that read, "From your Valentine," prompting us to set aside today to celebrate love. It came this year without the usual preparations. I'd foregone the traditions of this day for the medical traditions that we'd been experiencing. I had nothing for Larry. The usual stuffed animal and candy for Mathew hadn't been purchased.

With one hand on Christina's walker—the same walker we saw her have her first seizure in—and the other hand wrapped around the tall IV stand, we wheeled slowly around the nurses' station and down the corridor as far as we were allowed to go—never far enough. We rolled by rooms with children sitting on their beds and other little ones too sick to sit up where they lay teary and unhappy. Exhausted parents turned to look as we strode by. Doctors and nurses passed us. For the most part, they ignored us. When they did notice us, they briefly slowed and offered side-long glances before purposefully striding off.

I remembered when Larry had flown in from Texas; at that time, I was pregnant with Christina. As he emerged from the plane, his large hands gently grasped two stuffed bears with embroidered fabric hearts on their stomach. When their bellies were pressed, they played something like this, "Da-na- na- na na na, da na na na na na na, da na na na, l-o-v-e, that is what you mean to me—be my Valentine!" Mathew blasted out an animated laugh as Larry passed the bear to him. He embraced the stuffed animal and pressed the stomach over and over as we exited the airport. Those bears were still nestled in our home making us laugh every time they were played. This year, Valentine's Day had been altered. It almost seemed out of place and odd here in the hospital.

After six days without being able to eat or keep food down, it was magical watching Christina drink her first bottle. Although her little face looked pale and somewhat drawn, it was a huge relief knowing she was on the road to recovery.

The seizure frequency had increased again, and the neurologist expressed concern at how slowly she responded to anything. He was anxious for the genetic and metabolic tests to be returned with results. Samples of blood and urine were taken and sent to labs in Colorado, Minnesota, and Maryland. As the results began trickling in, one by one, it was like receiving the test score of a lifetime, only we prayed for them not to be positive.

Since seizure control dictated her release, EEGs were often and regularly first thing in the morning. It wasn't long during her recovery from the virus before she was again at status. We learned that there are four levels to an EEG result—Level I, II, III, and Status. Level I being the least amount of seizure activity to Status, the worst possible EEG result—requiring medical intervention and hospitalization. For Christina to be back at status showed us it was critical that we find seizure relief for her.

A breath of faith in the midst of this turbulent time came from the pastor of the church we had been attending since moving to Texas. Without fail, he showed up almost every day. He prayed with me, and many times, emotion got the best of me and I sobbed, feeling overwhelmed and tired. Still, I was hopeful. I shared with him the ketogenic diet that my sister had stumbled upon, showing him the two-page document the nurse had given me.

He slowly read through it.

"How do you feel about this?" he asked me.

"Something tells me that this is the answer for her. It 'feels' right." His benevolent demeanor knew exactly what I meant. "Her doctor listened to us when we told him about our discovery, and he seemed knowledgeable about the diet, but he did not want to put her on it. He explained that infants do not go on this diet and recommended trying all of the possible medications first, ruling them out one by one."

"I will keep this in my prayers so that God gives you and Larry the direction you need."

Without any family close, our pastor was the sole visitor who came faithfully each day. The conversation and prayerful support we relished with thankful hearts, knowing he had a 45-minute drive each way.

With his arms filled with bags and Mylar balloons floating above his head, their string attached to his hand, Larry had an "I have a surprise" look as he crept in the room. Mathew was so excited he kept leaping straight up, his blond hair flying. Like a puppy who expected a treat, he knew there was something fun in one of the bags. I imagined Larry teasing him on the way to the hospital, "I have something for you, buddy—but you'll have to wait until we get to mom and Christina." When Mathew took hold of one of the silver and red balloons floating in the air, with a serenity I wished for, he pranced around squeezing the bear snug under an arm. We dressed Christina in her Valentine's present: pink and purple heart pajamas. She snuggled happily in Larry's arms as her head followed the revolving Mylar balloon. For a few hours the heaviness of worry subsided, and we celebrated what we knew was constant and impenetrable, our love for each other.

Our Valentine "ball" was interrupted with a visit from Christina's neurologist, who had previously told us he was frustrated at the task of finding the right medication and was running out of options. Larry and I did not want to wait any longer. We were concerned at how much medication she had already been on— and to no avail.

Once again we asked the neurologist if we could try the ketogenic diet. We pleaded with him, actually. He was reluctant at first, stating again that infants do not go on this diet. Still, he couldn't give us any reasons why infants were restricted, so we persisted. We summarized the medications she had been on with no relief, and at last he let out a sigh, concluding that he would try anything that would help her.

Baby book entry: *February 14—Seven and-one-half months old:*
We decided today, Valentine's Day, that you are to go on a diet called the ketogenic. Tonight at 10:00 p.m. it will start. You will be given clear liquid or water until you go into ketosis–something

in the urine. We should see results in a few days. I've started calling people to pray for this diet to work. In the meantime you
are just beautiful. Sometimes, you smile. I can't wait to see what
you're like with no seizures for days. Mommy hasn't left your side.
Daddy and Mommy love, love, love you. We take your hand and
pray every day.

Larry was as excited as I was about starting the ketogenic
diet. He said, "I'm going to take half a day off and be here so I
can learn about the diet." His normally stoic face was turned up
into a smile—this holiday, though spent in a hospital, had taken a
positive turn. It *felt* like a holiday, and we had a reason to celebrate.
We began to hope.

The dietician was young. She wore a dark blue skirt and a
cloud-white blouse. The brown clipboard in her hand was obscured by paperwork, the pages and pages of notes that doctors
had taken about Christina and her condition. She told us her plan
was to develop a ketogenic formula since Christina was bottle fed.
The formula would be a mixture of a carbohydrate-free formula
and a fat emulsion, with vitamins and calcium being added by
prescription to maintain a healthy balance of nutrients.

We were ready to read or do anything in order to learn more
about the diet.

"Is there a handout available or information of any kind that
will help us understand the diet better?" I asked.

She hesitated, then explained she didn't have anything to give
us. We asked many questions about how to administer the diet
since if this worked, we would be taking her home and we would
be the ones formulating her diet. Her answer was vague. Neither
Larry nor I felt like we had a good understanding of the ketogenic diet, but we were nevertheless excited – in the same way
that most of us don't have an understanding of how a car works,

but are excited to purchase a new one. Larry took my hand and we smiled at each other as the young dietician began teaching us how to mix the ketogenic formula.

Five minutes into our meeting an abrupt knock interrupted the conversations and the door creaked open slightly. The dietician turned toward the door.

"Can I help you?"

"Are Mr. and Mrs. George in there with you?"

When Christina's neurologist entered the room we knew something was serious. His eyes were downcast and unblinking and he stood there, for a moment, without saying anything. We were afraid that he was going to say something dreadful.

"I am afraid that we are going to have to stop the diet. The test results have come back in today. I don't know why I didn't see this before." He said this like a student who had just made a mistake in class and was raising his hand again, confident that *this* time, the answer was correct.

"The results came back positive for MCAD (pronounced M—cad), and I believe…."

"What do you mean MCAD? What is that?" Larry interrupted.

"MCAD is a fatty acid oxidation defect. This isn't what I believe she has. However, I do think she has non-ketonic hyperglycinemia. I don't know why I didn't see this before. We will confirm this with the test we will perform tomorrow."

This sudden discovery was too unexpected, leaving us in a state of shock. In one fell swoop our hope in the diet was ripped away. A wave of weakness slid over my body, and I couldn't seem to find any words to speak.

"Non-ketonic hyperglycinemia is a metabolic disorder," the doctor offered.

"How bad is it?" Larry asked.

"In some cases it could be bad. Again, I would like to confirm this in the morning with a lumbar puncture," he said.

"Wait, I don't understand—what is the worst case and best case with this diagnosis?" My brain stalled and I fought to get the words out of my mouth in proper order.

The doctor elucidated, "Worst case is possible death, depending on the severity, but that can occur before one years old, and best case is we could manage it. There is typically some degree of mental retardation. Again, it all depends on the degree to which she has this disorder."

Larry and I looked at each other, our eyes wide and faces tense.

It wasn't computing, she was only eight months. Did he say she could die before turning one year old? *This cannot be happening*, I thought. *No, no! This is wrong.* I felt it. All wrong.

"This doesn't make sense. Wouldn't she have some kind of symptoms?" Larry's voice was pensive.

"Yes, seizures and most infants have apnea, typically from birth…."

"Apnea? What is that?" If there was an evident symptom to this disorder, surely I would know that she had it.

When he explained that apnea was an interruption in breathing while sleeping, my mind raced. Between moving from the house to the apartment, then into our newly built home, most of her little life she slept with Larry and me or inches away in her crib. Surely I would have known if she had stopped breathing.

The neurologist continued slowly, explaining that most babies with non-ketonic hyperglycinemia have what's called the neonatal form. They are lethargic and develop myoclonic seizures (brief shock-like jerks of muscle), apnea, and often die in their first year.

My mind began to shut down. I didn't want to hear any more, but he continued, explaining that babies who survive develop intractable (one of my most hated words) seizures and severe mental retardation (another most hated word). Symptoms might not even show up until the baby was about six months old. I assumed this was why he thought he had hit the jackpot of all diagnoses since Christina's seizures began at seven months.

Larry did not agree with this diagnosis any more than I did. "Can't she stay on the diet until we know for sure that this is the right diagnosis?" he asked.

"She can't. If I am right, and I am sure I am, this diet will harm her. This type of disorder mixed with the ketogenic diet will have a dangerous effect on her," the neurologist said.

We sat in silence for a moment until our words exploded and surprised us both when they were in unison.

"We need another opinion."

With one finger rubbing his chin the doctor pondered our request for a moment, allowing me a moment to regroup. I'd forgotten the dietician was still in the room. She sat frozen, tears rimming her eyes.

"I will schedule the lumbar puncture for first thing in the morning. In the meantime, there are very good genetic and meta-bolic specialists not far away, but I can't release her like this."

Realizing the lumbar puncture (commonly known as spinal tap) would be one more dreadful needle sting of the worst kind, I moaned out loud in dismay. Larry put his arm around me as we lifted off the chairs and proceeded alone to Christina's room.

It was as almost as if it was planned. Larry and I stood speechless on either side of our daughter's crib, reeling from the news. Just seconds after returning to the room, our pastor stood in the doorway, contemplating entering. Noticing the tears he spoke compassionately, "You must have gotten some bad news."

We both nodded in agreement, and Larry motioned in him.

Tightening my lips and glaring around the room I said, "I don't believe it. The symptoms are all wrong. She doesn't have this."

"Let's pray, then, for guidance." Bowing his head pastor led in prayer as we wept.

Uncertainty had been hurling us around since the onset of seizures, and fear taunted us daily. It all came crashing in while I was alone that night when Christina slept in her crib. Unable to sleep, nothing seemed right—I had felt so sure about the diet, everything inside had told me it was the answer for her. The arduous stay in the hospital and my separation from Mathew took their toll and my mind began to wander. *Are we being punished? Is this happening because of my sins from the past? Will she live with us forever? I hate seizures.* A painful part of my childhood haunted my early twenties and the decisions I made growing up, and in my early twenties were unhealthy and stupid at times. When things in life got tough, guilt plagued me, producing a faltering self esteem. Larry seemed to conquer those feelings through his strong support and unconditional love for me, but now in the depths of what we were in, I felt trapped and unable.

While Christina slept, I slipped into the bathroom and shut the door. I only intended to cry, but anger leapt out of me and I kicked the cinderblock wall with my sock-covered foot. I wrapped my hands into fists and pounded on that wall with all of my strength, as if *it* were the enemy, as if the hospital were the reason for Christina's sickness. Even though each blow hurt me, I hit the wall again, screaming until my voice cracked, "This cannot be – this is not happening!" After a time, I grew exhausted and pressed my back against the wall and slid to the ground. I grew bitter and cold toward God; my anger flickered toward the heavens. He wasn't helping my daughter. "Why aren't you helping her?" I shrieked, "I thought this diet was the answer for her – where are you?"

Suddenly a voice was heard: "This is not about you."

I was stunned for a second and even a bit frightened. Reaching up for the door handle, I turned it remaining on the floor. Pushing it open, I peered out, expecting to see a man standing outside the door. But no one was there except my little Christina, asleep on the bed. I felt confused and wondered, *What just happened? Am I losing it?*

Engulfed in the silence without any more strength left to put forth I began to realize something extraordinary had just happened. I felt His presence, He was there—there was no doubt and He was speaking to *me*.

"Oh, my God, You are here," I whispered barely audible. *Not about me? I know that.*

Pulling my knees to my chest, I sat soaking in the words I had just heard. *Was He telling me something?* I *chose* to listen. Not moving for several minutes, things began to become illuminated until suddenly things became clear, crystal clear—God was there, there on the floor with me. I was not alone—we had never been alone. It was true, I was a part of this journey, but it was not about me. This was about Christina, her future, not mine. Seeping into my grim thinking was the understanding that no matter how painful this was, no matter how inadequate I felt, I was her mother—this was my title, and I had my credentials, and this was not about me. Not that the pain or tears were wrong, because this illness hurt everyone involved, but I couldn't let the fear and anguish overtake me anymore. I'd been afraid to ask questions. *Why?* Was it because I felt inadequate? An honest answer was more than yes. Inadequate was just the beginning. Sinful, uneducated, naïve, beneath, and lack of confidence cumulated in my soul. Mixing with that was a pharisaical attitude toward doctors. "They were the ones who knew best, not us." I wasn't able to know or understand all that they did; therefore, they were the scholars in this situation. They called the plays, not me, and not Larry—we couldn't because they knew best.

Wrong. The inward part of me that was in such turmoil was in turmoil with good reason. Until I took the "me" out of the picture and realized that none of my self described inadequacies mattered. Why? The old saying, "with God all things are possible," rang true here. It would not be anything I could do, but it was something He could do. Whether we acknowledged it or not, we were all spiritual beings motivated by what was inside of us. Christina needed me to be there for her, I needed to "buck up" and be strong for her, she needed an *advocate*.

Suddenly, I began to feel remorse for my narcissistic way of thinking. I had to stop being a victim. It wasn't about me. Realizing this was the watershed that changed everything, from my way of thinking to the way treatment had been handled. Christina's care could no longer remain only under the charge of the medical profession. I would have to toughen up. No more holding back a question or not addressing concerns out of fear. The old saying, "doctor knows best," needed to be exiled.

Research and treatment choices needed to become our responsibility also—we could no longer leave these up to the doctors alone. Without a medical background, it would be difficult uncharted territory in the midst of a thunderous climate. However, no matter how difficult it would be, I realized, now, that this was not about me—and that we were not alone. Christina was God's child and so was Mathew. I had to remember that, no matter how inadequate or scared or overwhelming our daughter's illness became—it was still my job to be her advocate. That being said, the enormous privilege of being a parent didn't mean we had to go it alone.

Determination welled up. It was like grabbing a lifeline thrown from stable ground into water raging from a storm. Once taking hold, it alone secured the hope to survive. Realizing God was still in charge, that night, while crumpled on to the hospital bathroom floor, I took hold of the line of faith and did not let go.

"From this day foreword we never quite lost hope. We didn't doubt the medical findings of course, but there are too many inexplicable 'miraculous' cures for anyone, including doctors, to suppose that medicine has the last word." —Sheldon Vanauken, *A Severe Mercy*

Chapter Seven
Meteorology for Knowledge

"You may feel like a charred log in a fireplace, totally drained of energy, and unable to light a fire in yourself. Your personal inner resources appear to be exhausted. The first step toward rejuvenation begins with accepting where you are and exposing your poverty, frailty, and emptiness to the love that is everything."—Brennan Manning

IT WASN'T LIKE ANYTHING FELT before. I was made anew, given a new heart, given new desires. I felt refreshed and redeemed. It was as Isaiah wrote: "We shall rise on wings like eagles." I was once a passive robin, fleeing to the air whenever a doctor stepped near me. But God now made me into an eagle. My helplessness was gone. I knew, now, that God had not abandoned us, and I felt his empowerment. Instead of merely accepting other's words regarding Christina's condition and treatments, I was now committed to braving the medical storm, to becoming a meteorologist in order to understand epilepsy and seizures. Now that I knew we were not alone, a dark, smothering veil seemed to lift from my heart.

I opened the door to the bathroom and silently passed by Christina, who was still heavily medicated. I could feel my hair pinching and pulling at the back of my scalp. It must have been gnarled from scraping and sliding down the ragged bathroom walls. I rolled strands with my fingers as I approached the doors, but I left them be – other things were more pressing, now, than my appearance: I must have looked wild and war-like with my matted hair and eyes, bloodshot from stress and tears. I quietly opened the door and stepped into the hall. Approaching the nurses' desk, I cleared my throat, and asked, "How do I get information about epilepsy in children?"

The nurse's eyes flickered up from her scattered paperwork and she looked stunned. Perhaps I looked worse than I imagined. But, perhaps, she was surprised by the strength of my voice.

Slowly and carefully she spoke, remaining intentionally even toned. "There is a library here in the hospital for patient and family use. It's on the sixth floor."

The time had come to be an advocate for our daughter, and this was my first step in that direction. I felt a thrill roil through my chest. I was taking action.

She took her gaze off me long enough to check her watch. It was after 8:00 p.m. I was sure she was going to tell me that the library was already closed or, worse yet, that there wasn't anyone available to sit with Christina. Thankfully, the words never came. She merely nodded and asked for a few minutes to find someone.

As the elevator made its way up to the sixth floor I couldn't help but wonder, *How could we have not known there was a library here in the hospital?* Perhaps before today, it wouldn't have mattered anyway.

"Hello, may I help you?" The woman with a servile smile behind the desk seemed ready and eager to be of assistance.

"Yes, I would like any information you can give me on non-ketonic hyperglycinemia and epilepsy."

"All right," she said lifting her pen. She began jotting down my request, "And this is for an adult?"

"No, this is for my child."

"Well, we have all kinds of information here for children. Let's see here, your child is how old?"

"Seven-and-a-half months," I replied.

I'm not sure why, but it seemed to get even quieter in the library as she peered upwards at me for a closer look. She gazed compassionately for a moment, then as if she remembered what she was supposed to be doing, quickly looked down and began flipping through reference pages. She looked through books pulled from shelves and zeroed in on a few pages.

"Can I run some copies for you?" she asked, thumbing through them. "There are two articles here that I think you might find helpful on non-ketonic hyperglycinemia, and numerous ones on epilepsy. I will give you the first few and then a list of the rest, okay?"

I was relieved that she would copy those pages. Even though I asked to go to the library, it felt strange leaving Christina—I was glad not to be gone long. This time on the same elevator down, I felt a twinge of empowerment.

The articles led me through a tangled labyrinth of genetic and metabolic disorders as I sought to barricade Christina from the onslaught of seizures, but it was difficult to find help in the web of medical jargon. I learned about and understood some disorders, but I was confused by others. The more I ventured in, however, the more I was convinced that we needed another doctor's opinion.

With his hand rubbing his chin, the neurologist seemed bewildered.

"I can't release her like this."

After reading some of the documents given to me from the librarian, it was clear that we had to have a second opinion from a genetic and metabolic expert. The only one we could find in the area was across town at Santa Rosa hospital, twenty minutes away.

After a long uncomfortable pause he continued, "I will allow her to leave for further evaluation, but she will need to be transported by ambulance under medical supervision."

As the stretcher was unloaded from the ambulance with Christina on it in front of Santa Rosa Hospital, I fought off emotion and feelings of being a victim, reminding myself there was a job to do. It didn't matter what people thought, and there were plenty looking in our direction—I didn't care. This wasn't about me. The doubt that was a part of my old self ebbed and slipped away, revealing the beautiful, glistening hope flickering with the remembrance of my conversation with God.

Christina shifted her body and flailed her arms frantically; her eyes leaped back and forth, as if she were trying to understand the reason for a troubling change. But when her little eyes caught sight of Larry walking in through the hospital doors, she smiled excitedly. When she smiled, there was no doubt she knew us—a positive clue to her thinking ability, now in question under the guise of the haunting diagnosis we desperately wanted to disprove. Larry wrapped his warm hand over mine as it held on to the gurney where Christina lay as it was wheeled about. He was anxious to hear more about the information the librarian had given me. I had dissected it, read thoroughly through it and even understood a few medical terms that I had heard and wondered about. Larry supported my research and trusted along with me that this would prove valuable. As we waited in a room for the specialist, I eagerly recalled as much as I could.

"She does not have this, I just know it, I feel it."

"Honey, I hope you're right." His voice waivered like a violin string.

Bending, he kissed Christina, now snuggled on my lap, and then me. It seemed as though he was unable to speak, trying to remain stoic, but his tired cobalt blue eyes gave way to heavy emotions.

Neither of us knew what to expect, especially from a genetics doctor—the kind of doctor we didn't even know existed until the day before. When the door opened and a woman walked in, eagerly shaking both of our hands and emanating a warm smile and pleasant disposition, we both looked at each other as if happily to say, *I wasn't expecting this.* She listened compassionately to our concerns.

I began, "Christina doesn't fit the profile. Recently, I read information on non-ketotic hyperglycinemia, and I just don't see the symptoms she should be having."

Just when I thought the doctor was going to challenge what I said, she again impressed us with her compassionate and understanding tone. "I am inclined to agree with you that she does not fit the profile for the more severe version of this disorder,"

She spoke calmly, flipping back and forth through the pages included in the file sent from the neurologist. Her gaze lingered longer than I would have liked on the report indicating positive for MCAD. She took several quiet minutes digesting and researching the notes, EEG and various other test results.

When she finished, she concluded, "What should be done next is for us to draw our own samples here. I would like to send them to a few different labs across the country. There are labs that have a high degree of accuracy and insight into these kinds of disorders. I would like to utilize them for this. Of course, this involves drawing blood and fluids again from here." She paused. "Mr. and Mrs. George, are you all right with this?"

Although we didn't want to submit Christina to any more discomfort, having a proper diagnosis was important. I looked at Larry. Both of us worried about how much Christina had already endured—we were weary of it all, but knew we had to consent to this if we were to be assured of a proper diagnosis. We agreed.

After they drew blood and took urine via a catheter, Larry headed back to the office and Christina and I returned with the EMT to "our" hospital—or second home as it had become.

⊰⊱

Her steel crib was filled with stuffed animals and toys from home, but was not furnished with bumper pads. Many times the seizures caused her to sit up and "jack knife" forward. Her face would land on the bed or the bars of the steel crib if I couldn't reach her in time. For some reason staff couldn't find pads; so, the nurse propped up pillows, taping them in place with surgical tape. More than once, I felt like packing her up and leaving.

Drawing blood from Christina became a fine art. When a tech in training had tried to draw blood but couldn't, we advocated for our daughter. It was the weekend and thankfully Larry and Mathew were at the hospital. No doubt about it, we didn't like the jacket, but using it brought to light another concern. Between the intractable seizures and needle pokes, the "unnatural" behavior Christina was exhibiting—not fighting when in pain, and crying while smiling during a seizure—made us worry that the 'dots,' so to speak, were not connecting properly in Christina's brain. I wondered if this was the reason she wasn't fighting back. After several attempts at drawing blood, with minimal objection from Christina, I turned to Larry in anguish.

"We have to stop this."

Larry did just that. The head nurse was called in and after a heated discussion, hospital staff left—without drawing blood. We more than understood the need for training, and appreciated everything. But Christina had endured so much we could no longer allow her to be a part of their training anymore.

Recalling what the head nurse told us about the jacket, "It is hospital policy. Without it, a child could move—it is in the child's best interest." Even though nothing came of my concern, voicing it was another stride toward advocacy, and that was equitable.

"Do you see it? Right there—oh, and here again!" exclaimed the technician administering the EEG. He pointed to the paper feeding out of the machine. The tall lanky neurologist bent over his shoulder intently watching as the results exited the machine.

"Beautiful, aren't they?" He smiled as the needles continued plotting their information on the paper. There was a hint of delight in his voice. "Sleep spindles, good—first time we've seen these!"

"What are they?" I asked, eager to understand.

"The EEG is showing that Christina is sleeping, a rested sleep pattern is emerging: sleep spindles."

Depakote ® (or the generic name, Valproic Acid), Phenobarbital, Dilantin (Phenytoin), Tegretol ® (Carbamazepine) and Topomax (Lamotrigene), were anti-seizure medications that became commonly used and spoken of. Chemicals meant to triumph over seizures, but had so far, been useless.

Three weeks after witnessing the frightening seizures that began in the bathtub, Christina began drifting off to sleep wrapped snuggly in a blanket in my arms. Electrodes attached to her head fed into the EEG as needles streamed back and forth on paper. While trying to find a medication that worked, the neurologist injected a medication called Klonopin® (or clonazepam) into the IV. The EEGs were intentionally given while she was awake, then they would record as she fell to sleep. Falling in and out of sleep was a vulnerable time for seizure activity. They often increased as she went in and out of sleep mode. Often she would wake up after sleeping for 20 minutes with a series of seizures. Now I understood why she had been fussy—what, if any, rested sleep had she been getting?

Sleep spindles. A term I had never heard of, but loved in an instant.

The spindles indicated the new medication slowed the seizure activity. It was news we had been praying for.

Baby Book entry: February 20th, 7 months 23 days old

The medication actually slowed the seizures and you had sleep spindles. Sleep spindles mean you have rested sleep…how long it has been since you have slept soundly?

———◆———

With plastic food on a tiny plastic plate in front of us, Mathew and I sat across from each other celebrating our "pretend" welcome home meal at the table in his room. The brightness of the clear day warmed up the room as he dished out the plastic food. We pretended to eat.

"Yum, this is good!" I exclaimed.

Instantly Mathew rose from his chair and reached for my plastic drumstick. He pretended to eat it. There was something about serving plastic food that amazed him, he was having a ball. Every few minutes he would walk to Christina who was lying on the floor and softly put his hand on her, brush her cheek tenderly, as I had done, smile right in her face holding his face close to hers and kiss her.

I was happy to be home, in clean socks from my own drawer with clean clothes and the ability to shower whenever I wanted. Christina was easier to change without IV's to work around and, with lessened seizures, she seemed happier. Life was better at home.

Whenever the phone rang, it reminded us we were waiting for results—results that could change our future. One minute we couldn't wait for it to ring, the next we hoped it wouldn't. Preparing lunch after a sleep-deprived night filled with seizures, I grabbed the phone and began dialing my grandmother's number. *What am I doing?* For a moment, it evaded me that she was gone and I couldn't call her anymore. Stress made memories and clear thinking harder. It was a constant job to keep things in perspective. Fear, with its crippling effect, was not an option, though I struggled with it every day.

Within two weeks of being home, phone calls came trickling in with results from both the neurologist and the genetic and metabolic specialist. Each new phone call gave the most recent test results back from the different labs. When the spinal fluid results came in, the neurologist heaved a sigh of disbelief when he told me the news, *negative* for non-ketonic hyperglycinemia. Tears of joy silently gravitated down as he continued to explain that none of the test results were positive—so far. He was confused, thinking surely he had found a disorder. Within 24 hours of his call, the genetics and metabolic specialist telephoned. She was also surprised but happy to report that none of the tests came back positive for any genetic or metabolic disorder. Flashing back to the horrible day when the neurologist announced his devastating diagnosis, I realized this was a precarious storm we were in. It seemed as though we had weathered powerful gusts, and we weren't in the storm alone. Are these *prayers answered*?

Christina had been tested for every genetic and metabolic disorder she could have fit the profile for. Her seizures were now considered "idiopathic," meaning no known cause. Rushing to Larry when he came home from work, I threw my arms around his neck and he wrapped me in a hug. My cheek brushed against his short beard that ran along his jaw line. Larry lifted Mathew, who wanted to be included in the festivities. Larry lifted him as high as he could above his head. Mathew stretched out his arms like he was flying and laughed. We were ecstatic knowing Christina did not have a disorder that could take her life. It felt as though we had triumphed over the terrifying whirlwind diagnosis.

I wondered where we would be if we hadn't requested that second opinion. Would we have believed the results? There was no doubt that researching to find evidence to disprove a lethal diagnosis, and requiring a second opinion was empowering—especially now. Instead of focusing on what we couldn't do, the tables turned in our favor when what could be done was done. Just when I thought yelling loudly and throwing a tantrum was unheard or unseen, the reality that God never left and knew everything was never as real to me as it was then. I knew now that those feelings I had before leaving Minnesota, the ones I discounted and tried to forget, were not because I was stressed. And I realized that whenever the fog rolled in, the storm would be best managed on my knees.

Reading the book, "Seizures and Epilepsy in Childhood: A Guide for Parents" by John Freeman, M.D., Eileen P.G. Vinning, M.D., and Diana J. Pillis, was like stepping through a gold mine and finding nuggets with each turn—only the nuggets were on the pages. The information on seizures gave a basic understanding that previously, hadn't been shared with us. *Knowing the facts and learning statistics* changed the future treatment for Christina.

1. "In more than half of the cases of seizures in childhood, no cause can be found." (p. 196).

2. "For most children seizures are not uncontrollable, they are only difficult to control. ... Many times parents of children with difficult to control seizures who persisted in looking for the right therapy turned 'uncontrollable' seizures into controlled seizures." (p. 230)

3. "For 80 percent of children with epilepsy, seizures can be controlled...Epilepsy never causes cerebral palsy and seldom causes mental retardation." (p.223)

Dr. Freeman, the first author listed, was the real life doctor who treated the child with epilepsy in the movie "First Do No Harm," the movie my sister had told me about. The film was inspired by Charlie Abrahams, who also had intractable epilepsy. The ketogenic diet was the only treatment that controlled his seizures.

Chapter eight
The Ketogenic Beginning

Advocate: "A person who pleads for or in behalf of another; intercessor"
—Dictionary.com unabridged.

I ONCE SAW A RUSTIC sign in a laundromat, "The only thing normal here is the button on the washing machine." By the time Christina was ten months old, the sign described our family. But unlike the washing machine, we did not even have a working normal *button*. We were being cleaned by the abrasive trials of life. Once, we were the average couple with two kids and a house, and Larry and I would hire a sitter and have date night.

But now – how things had changed! We rarely left the house, and certainly not for dates. The lights would blink on and off during the night as we dealt with Christina's seizures and anxious truck drivers who needed Larry's immediate assistance. We added a third child on weekends – Whitney.

She brought clothing and schoolwork, and had her own bedroom, which doubled as our guestroom and office. It may have seemed odd to some people, but to us she was a blessing, a welcome extension of our family. Her mom needed help juggling things, and we stepped up to open our home to her. At times, I felt guilty because we seemed to get the better end of the deal as Whitney loved Mathew and Christina and didn't want anything more than to be with them—she kept Mathew busy and occupied, something he desperately needed.

Even trips to the grocery store changed. Many times we would be forced to dash to the exit of the local Albertson's due to an onset of seizures. I'm sure the employees often wondered why this woman would abandon her cart loaded with groceries.

One time, as we hurried up and down the grocery aisle, I noticed a gaggle of women next to pasta boxes. At first, I paid little attention—but I suddenly realized that their furtive glances and hushed whispers were directed at us. My heart sank. They were staring at my beautiful little girl and the bruises on her forehead.

A few days before, a seizure had struck without warning. Christina had banged her head against the bookshelf. These shoppers were seeing the blue, brown, and yellow hues staggering across her forehead, and they were convinced she'd been abused.

I was mortified at what they assumed.

A new world of understanding opened to me. I didn't like feeling judged unfairly, and I understood now what this was like. Here in this grocery store, without being able to share our story, I was helpless; however, I could work to find a cure for Christina's seizures.

Through research, I learned that some children who have this type of seizure (atonic drops) wore helmets, but for Christina, her muscles weren't strong enough to hold her head up with the weight of the helmet. We tied padding along the perimeter of her crib, and placed soft toys and cushions on the trays of her walker and high chair.

On paper, Christina's seizures showed she was out of status, the EEG reading where immediate medical attention needed to be given, but each day and night was filled in anticipation of the next seizure. Medication was increased to a dangerous level. We managed to weather the storm, but it was prayer that covered us like an umbrella while it rained.

Vivian Green once said, "Life isn't about waiting for the storm to pass….it's about learning to dance in the rain." We weren't dancing. This storm for us was more like trudging through the thickest, muck, sludge and slime where we'd—unlike the graceful dancer—slip and fall face down in despair.

Larry and I grieved that each day with seizures and so many chemicals that were debilitating in themselves was another lost day of development. Still, the neurologist was confident about mixing medication to find seizure control. I wasn't convinced. We continued to be meteorologists, learning about the storm and beginning to plot a new course of action.

Dressed up for picture day at preschool, Mathew resembled a naval officer in formal attire. Blue polyester jacket with an epaulette and golden buttons fitted perfectly over his white shirt and blue pinstripe pants. I parted his blond hair wondering if it would stay this color.

Christina's gold shoes slipped out from under sapphire blue velvet ruffles. The preschool invited siblings to have their pictures taken also. Secured in car seats, we headed down I-35 toward San Marcos. In 70 mile an hour traffic, I looked in the rear-view mirror. Christina's face was empty and barren with the look of a seizure. Her head plummeted forward hitting the padded arm of her seat. The early morning traffic was heavy, and I wasn't in the right lane to pull over. It took me by surprise and I had to decide—pull over in dangerously busy traffic or keep going.

I forged ahead in panic.

Stopping in the parking lot, I flung open the driver's side door and shot out of the car not bothering to close the door. Pulling open Christina's door, I unlatched and slid her out of the seat and into my arms.

Mathew looked at me bewildered. His lips pursed, and tears slipped out. His little hands reached for mine, and together we wiped them away. He unbuckled himself and slid out of his seat.

"It's okay now. Matt, are you okay?" I forced a smile. His face softened and he smiled back. "Ready to have your picture taken?"

"Yessss!" he squealed. Thankfully, once inside the familiar brick preschool setting, he he joined friends at a table of Crayons and paper. And carried on as if nothing had happened.

After washing Christina's face and straightening up her outfit, we went to the room where pictures were being taken. As the photographer readied the camera, I placed my arm behind Christina, keeping her sitting stable when the bright light of the camera flashed.

It was late that night when Larry and I crawled into bed. He reached over and pulled me close. He was the man I'd prayed for, who loved me unconditionally. The strong bond was still there, but our relationship had suffered due to our trials, and we were both throbbing in emotional pain over Christina's illness. Our words were sluggish and somber as we discussed her illness.

After the terrifying seizures that happened in the car, we both agreed something more needed to be done for her. "Why hadn't her doctor suggested starting the ketogenic diet again since no genetic or metabolic disorders were found? Why can't we have her on the diet again? The last conversation we had with Christina's doctor about seizure control he asked us to give the medication more time even though he admitted the she was given a dose higher than what was considered safe. Even with this knowledge her doctor didn't want to put her on the diet.

"Check back with me in a few days, okay?" was the doctor's disconnected reply.

Larry and I faced each other, our heads resting on soft pillows. His deep voice grew ragged as he asked me about Christina's development.

"What do you mean she isn't reaching milestones?"

Mathew obviously had developed much more quickly than Christina. At the age of ten months, had begun mastering walking. We often chased after him because his feet worked more quickly than his mind, and he was forever stumbling over things. But Christina wasn't yet bearing weight on her legs. Then there was talking or babbling. Mathew met all of the appropriate babbling skills and talking, but Christina did not utter a word or sound other than crying. I had purchased a book when Mathew was born about child development in the first year and recovered it from the nightstand draw. I tried to find consolation in the pages, but couldn't. Mathew had made each milestone on or ahead of the suggested age, but Christina was different—starkly different. Larry didn't want me to be discouraged and was trying to find the right words to help.

"It's just the medication. Once she is stable, she'll start developing."

Deflated, and not seeing anything positive at the moment, I set the book back in the drawer of the nightstand drawer and thrust it shut.

Quietly I crabbed, "I don't ever want to look at that book again."

We'd easily understand if the medication slowed her development, but it didn't explain her other odd behaviors. She'd smile, at times, but not always intentionally. Much of the time she was obviously distant, like we were specks on her mind's horizon. From time to time she would interact with us when we'd draw close and make a silly face. But it was rare that she'd laugh, and when she did, it was like a longing, beautiful melody. We tried to make eye contact, but it was seldom our eyes caught hers. She tightened often, and did not seem to want to be held or cuddled. We wondered if she didn't want to be touched. She began slapping the same button on a musical toy with large buttons, over and over again, until her hand became red. When I removed the toy, she

continued to pound the ball of her hand the same way onto the
tray of her walker. At times, I had to lift her out of the walker to
stop the pernicious behavior.

Larry and I were anxious and could not immediately fall asleep,
so we began to chart our plan. We'd seen the medications not
working, and we were determined to be her advocates. We could
no longer permit our daughter another day of waiting. It was not a
difficult decision, but one we knew would lead to a discussion with
a less than eager doctor to prescribe the ketogenic diet.

We held hands and prayed before drifting off to sleep.

The next day after demanding that Christina be put on the
diet, the doctor knew he could not change our minds. Seven days
later Christina was admitted to the hospital to initiate the diet.

Seeing the dietician rekindled the memory of when the neurologist came crashing in to our meeting announcing his discovery of the life-threatening metabolic disorder.

"I'm so glad the test results were wrong," the dietician said,
while slowly closing the door.

I knew she was the key to unlocking the diet for us, but
wondered if she realized this as she didn't appear enthusiastic or
passionate about starting the diet, which I would have preferred,
she seemed ready.

To initiate the diet Christina needed to fast. Withholding was
hard, but necessary we were told, in order for her body to go
into ketosis—burning fat for energy instead of carbohydrates and
sugar. Ketones become present in the blood and urine when our
bodies begin to burn fat. That's when we would begin feeding
her the ketogenic formula.

I understood it this way: when the body burns fat for energy,
it leaves an 'ash' in the blood and urine. This waste is called ketones. I had read that for most children on the diet, the higher the

level of ketones, or the more fat they burn for energy, the better the seizure control.

Two days after being admitted, Christina's body had just begun to pass low amounts of ketones when she became lethargic. Her blood sugar level was dangerously low and needed a few ounces of juice to bring it up.

The male nurse who was in charge of Christina went to get the juice, and I left Larry in the room with the baby while I tried to find the dietician. When I returned, Christina was drinking the last of the juice in a bottle.

"He gave her only two or three ounces, right?" I asked.

Larry looked stunned. "What do you mean two or three ounces of juice? He gave me two bottles. This is the last of the second one."

It was too much. Way too much. "The instructions the dietician and neurologist left were supposed to read 'only two or three ounces.'" I moaned.

Larry pushed the nurses' call button. When the nurse came back, he had no idea what I was talking about. In fact, he didn't seem even to know what kind of diet she was being put on. Then a second nurse came in, one who had been Christina's nurse several times in the past. She didn't know how much juice was to be given, either. They both flipped through the chart, and read out loud this sentence: "If blood sugar drops below"..."then juice is to be given and the doctor called."

Larry was feeling awful. But it wasn't his fault; in fact, we were beginning to realize that we had been presumptuous in assuming that the staff tending to her care knew the protocol of this specialized diet. In fact, it didn't seem that anyone really knew this diet at all. With the neurologist, dietician, and head nurse outside Christina's door, Larry and I discussed with them the ketogenic diet and how it was supposed to be initiated. What stunned us the most was the response from the dietician. She had no idea how much juice to give if blood sugar dropped.

"You have worked with this diet before—right?" I asked.

When she explained it was the first time she had ever worked with the diet, I began to worry for the wellbeing of my child.

Larry came close to a shout, "This is wrong. No one should be taking care of her who does not know what he or she is doing."

When the meeting ended, Larry and I were left alone. We realized that no one at the hospital—nurses or doctors—knew the ketogenic diet. We were disturbed that the staff failed to disclose this crucial fact.

If they had said that this was the first time but they would be willing to try it, we could have made our decision from there. Now it was too late and, again, Christina was paying the price.

We talked about taking her where the diet was developed, just a few hours from where we used to live in Minnesota. For most of our lives we lived two hours away from Mayo Clinic, and now that we needed its expertise, we were twelve hundred miles away. We thought back to that August day when Christina was a newborn and we were leaving Minnesota for Texas, when the starter had gone out in the car. There was no doubt now for either of us that those strange and uncomfortable feelings I'd felt meant something.

We both desperately wanted our daughter on this diet. The ketogenic diet seemed our only hope left. Medications had failed her, and surgery wasn't an option for seizure control since seizure activity was generalized.

Larry had had enough. His patience was gone. He was like a balloon stretched to capacity: at any moment, he could burst. He talked to the dietician with sad eyes and a firm voice and said, "She will not be put at risk, again! If you are not an expert with the diet, then we need direction from someone who is. Otherwise, we're going home."

The dietician swallowed hard, "There is a dietician in Houston. She knows the diet. I've already been in contact with her. She will help us start the diet and will take this on as a consult in order to help us."

"We'll do this only because you're collaborating with her. In the meantime, Christina needs a break. We want her to have a regular diet for a day, and then we can proceed."

Looking at my husband, I couldn't have loved him more just then.

"One more thing," I interjected, "no one should enter her room, nor give her anything from now on, unless that reason has checked the chart and the instructions are clearly given."

The fourth day in the hospital Christina's seizures were still raging on as her little body was making the transition from burning carbohydrates to burning fat. During the time without food, we managed to regulate her blood sugar with intermittent sips of juice, and she did just fine.

When the door opened and a nurse walked in holding a bottle which I knew was the first meal with ketogenic formula, I fought back tears. Wrapping my baby in a blanket together Christina and I sank into the chair in the room. I couldn't wait to feed her. The past four days had been agonizing for me, it was unnatural for a mother to withhold food from her child. But I stayed the course, since another part of me said, "This is the answer you've been looking for." The bottle looked so normal, eggshell color formula, which was a blend of carbohydrate free formula and a fat emulsion that would continue the fasting state. Lowering the nipple to her lips, she opened her little mouth and tasted it for the first time. She hesitated for a moment. Her lips wrapped around the nipple and she began sucking in the formula as she would have any other bottle. While she drank, I thanked God for this diet.

Christina was started at a ratio of three to one: three parts fat to one part carbohydrate and protein. She was given a sugar-free multi-vitamin and a calcium supplement prescribed by the neurologist. These supplements were given according to her weight, and, together, were the nutrients she needed to survive. At the same time, the formulation kept her metabolism in a constant state of fasting.

By day six of this hospitalization we'd had two successful days on the diet without a setback and Christina was released.

Was it our imagination? Within days of being home, the seizures seemed to be less frequent, but neither Larry nor I were dancing in the rain just yet.

The dietician rarely returned my phone calls and, when she did, it was clear that she was struggling with the intricacies of the diet. The neurologist was unhelpful. When we asked him questions, he pointed us back to the dietician, saying, "It's her project. Give it time."

Christina was nearing her first birthday, and she'd been possessed by raging seizures for nearly half of her life. We wanted this diet to work, but needed help from a medical staff that had a better standard of care. We began to contemplate a return to Minnesota.

Larry was up to something, I could tell by the precarious grin on his face. When he pulled into a car dealership, I was confused.

"What are we doing here?"

"Just trust me." He always said this when he wanted to surprise me.

He pulled up in a blue van minutes later. "What do you think?" he asked.

"Why are we—?" Then it hit me, "Are you thinking, a new vehicle is needed for a trip?"

He wasted no time shaking his head yes. My heart flooded with thankfulness for my husband. He knew it was not possible to take off too much time, or he would risk losing his job, and medical insurance, yet he wanted to provide a way for us to make the trip. As he handed the keys to our old Chevy to the salesperson, I knew we wouldn't have to worry about the starter or something else going out, the way it did before we left Minnesota. He pulled out paperwork with numbers strewn all over it. He checked the cost of flights and compared them to travel by vehicle. He ran the miles and gas, as he does every day at work for his truck drivers and concluded the best way financially for us. This was it.

We set an appointment for Christina to be seen by a neurologist at Mayo Clinic, 1,200 miles away.

Whitney holding Christina on her first birthday.
On her left Jamie and Jodi, on her the right, Amanda, Kara and Kayla.

Chapter Nine
Like a Deer Running Through Woods

"At the timberline where the storms strike with the most fury, the sturdiest trees are found." —Hudson Taylor

WARM AIR FROM A CLEAR July day brushed my face as I bent my neck back to scan the enormous grey building, home to Mayo Clinic. The clinic hovered over us eclipsing other buildings as we stood across the street near the entrance of our hotel, freshly arrived from a two day trip. Larry's arms wrapped around Christina, fresh out of her car seat, the strap of a diaper bag was slung over my shoulder as I held onto Mathew's hand. We all looked up. The gigantic building rose into the cerulean blue sky, reminding me of the Sears Tower. Gigantic slabs of battle ship grey marble formed parts of the exterior, and a massive bronze sculpture of a man, arms stretched upward, evoking the humaneness of us all protruded from the exterior several floors up.

A uniformed bellhop came rushing out to greet us. "Can I help you with the luggage, sir?"

"Ah—yes," Larry answered shifting his attention away from the building.

"It's quite a sight, isn't it?" the bellhop said smiling, "You here for the clinic?"

"Yes, we are."

Larry and the bellhop began emptying the van. Luggage, baby bottles—some needing to be washed—a box of carbohydrate free formula and another with glass bottles of microlipid (fat emulsion). They clinked together as they were lifted on to the luggage carrier. When the men finished, only two carseats and Cheerios scattered on the car's carpeting were left.

Burgundy and gold carpet rolled across the reception area floor distracting the eye with its paisley design. A lingering smell of old cigars and air freshener mixed with newer carpet and filtered air. This hotel, although beautiful, seemed hardly the place for two young children, but we ignored it— it was the clinic, not the hotel, and relief from the seizure storm that had brought us to this lobby.

Morning arrived too soon, Larry and I, exhausted from the long drive and months of seizures, could have slept longer. But we pulled ourselves out from the covers and left the hotel soon enough to eat breakfast at Mayo's cafeteria. Inside the building, we stood looking like tourists until a man dressed in a navy-colored suit with a Mayo Clinic badge greeted us.

"Can I direct you to where you need to go?"

I couldn't help sensing a calm feeling I had come over me upon entering the building. The feeling was more than a reaction to the spacious room, organic curves and clear glass ceilings. It was a feeling that *this is where we are supposed to be.*

At the registration desk we gave our insurance information and filled out necessary paperwork before walking toward the elevators for Christina's first appointment. High ceilings, marble floors, bronze door handles and works of art—this was nothing like we expected. Beauty graced every corner, from blown glass artwork to ancient artifacts behind glass.

Nearly six months of seizures, tortuous needle pokes, debilitating medications, and a life-threatening misdiagnosis, had brought us here. The 1,200 mile trek seemed halfway round the world in our new azure minivan by the time we reached Rochester. We traveled on hope—hope that inside this mammoth grey building we would find the right care for our daughter, whose life was being ripped away by a tornado of relentless seizures. We wanted someone to help us stop this tornadic villain, render it weak and unable to continue. Could this enormous grey building hold the key to seizure freedom? We hoped it did—everything was at stake. But here were hundreds of the best doctors and scientists in the world. My heart raced, and I was certain my blood pressure elevated. I felt small and inadequate, but remembering my night on the bathroom floor, I realized God was with me. I wasn't alone that night, and we weren't alone here. We are never alone—any of us.

The first appointment was on the floor called east nine with the neurologist. A tall dark haired doctor in his thirties compassionately interrogated us, jotting notes on a clipboard resting on his one knee. When he finished, the questions he asked tugged at a place inside of me I didn't know existed. *Why did he ask so many questions about previous testing? Was he looking for the cause of the seizures?* I did not want any more testing. No known cause was found. It conflicted with those first months of seizures when I couldn't stand not knowing the cause. Now, after six months of weathering the seizure storm, the unknown was comfortable.

Mathew drew a crayon portrait while one year old Christina sat with her back supported by one of Larry's legs. She was on the floor pushing a stroller wheel around and around. When the large wooden door slowly opened, Larry began to reach for her.

"No, no, leave her there—she is fine." With half of his body in the room, the doctor's eyes lingered on our daughter until he slipped through the door stepping over Christina.

A subtle Spanish accent punctuated his words when Dr. Gomez introduced himself. His tanned skin was aged. He was older than I imagined, and not my idea of the appropriate age of doctor would be best for our child. I'd hoped for someone fresh out of med school. After all, that person would know all the newest and latest treatments.

Larry and I explained our journey to Mayo Clinic was to perfect the diet for Christina.

"We can do that. However, I have looked over the test results done before you arrived here and we are confident with the blood work, but we want to have another MRI done. The one you brought is of poor quality. I'd like clearer imaging done."

I looked at Larry. He returned my gaze wondering what I was thinking. *We don't want any more testing. She doesn't have anything wrong with her—they couldn't find anything.*

After lifting Christina onto the examining table, he shut the lights off and scanned her bare body with a Wood's lamp (ultraviolet light).

"Do you see this small area where there is no pigment?" He pointed to the middle of her back where a small leaf shape had been since birth. It was lighter than her normal skin tone.

"This type of birthmark is found in a condition called tuberous sclerosis. Typically there is more than one. Even so, I'm going to test her for this since it has not been done. Okay?"

Larry and I looked to the other for a decision, then simultaneously agreed.

With calmness and clarity, Dr. Gomez answered all of the questions and concerns we had listed before the appointment, from throwing up, to the toxic levels of medications, to our desperation for help with the diet.

"Let's finish this testing and work on getting the seizures under control," he stated.

With the appointment itinerary in hand, we left east nine to coordinate the next three days of testing. Most of it would be without my husband. His boss was not interested in extending time off, and Larry worried that if he lost his job, it would be the end of medical benefits—benefits we couldn't afford to be without. Larry was only able to drive us up and stay one day before heading back home to work. Huddled together, Mathew squeezed in between us, Larry's warm arms felt comfortable and safe—I didn't want to be here without him, but we both knew there was no other choice.

"Grandma!"

Mathew screamed when he caught sight of my mother in law, Jane walking down the hallway. Red, blue, and gold colors swirled on the shawl draped over her shoulders. The light silk edges floated as she rushed toward her grandson for a hug. She had driven two hours to accompany me here during appointments—the first being the MRI.

After Christina drank a purple liquid anesthesia, she sat calmly on my lap. Her right hand reached up and her fingers caressed my lips. I wondered if it comforted her. The nurse lifted the stethoscope off her neck and over her light brown hair. When she placed it on Christina's chest—it reminded me of something painful, eerie, and dim; something I didn't want to remember, but couldn't help as the stethoscope cleverly reminded me of the terrifying previous MRI, when the doctor didn't speak to us and Christina seemed frozen in a seizure.

A man dressed in a white lab coat entered the room and introduced himself as the doctor performing the MRI. He asked how things were, I stumbled on words trying to shake myself out of a near self induced panic haunted by the writhe of the doctor from the first MRI.

"Okay," was all that I could muster.

He brushed his hand warmly on Christina's head, observing her medication induced groggy state. Her head moved slightly, tucking into me. When he asked if I had any questions before they started, I realized this was a different level of care than we had previously been exposed to, and this MRI experience would be different.

Once asleep, the nurse lifted Christina was lifted by the nurse out of my arms. She took her to the MRI room, next door. An hour later, she returned asking for me to sign a release to use dye.

I almost signed my name, but stopped. Why now? Laying the pen down, I requested more information.

The doctor came quickly and explained he was having difficulty viewing certain areas. "An MRI can be tricky. It's almost like a deer running in the woods. One minute you see him, the next you don't. In order to get a clearer picture, I need to use the dye." I didn't want to sign the form. *We didn't come here for this. She already had this test, and her brain was fine.*

The truth was, I was afraid they would find something. Couldn't we just leave well enough alone? I wrestled with inner assaults of fear, but knew what I had to do. Jeremiah said it clearly when he wrote, "You can't heal a wound by saying it's not there!" Jeremiah 6:14 (TLB). We had to be sure of what was and wasn't there. Gulping down fear, I penned my name and handed the form back to the doctor.

Mathew crawled into my lap put his hands on my cheeks, pushing them together in an attempt to form a smile. I wasn't in the smiling mood, and he could tell.

"What?" he inquired, surveying the worry etched on my face. This didn't seem fair to him. Time with Grandma was supposed to be fun. Being here in a hospital with her was not normal for him. I hugged him until he leaped over the chair and onto Jane's lap.

When the test was complete, the doctor seemed positive, stating the dye gave a much clearer image. A string of appointments followed during the next 24 hours from an eye examination by a pediatric ophthalmologist and cardiologist, to check for tubors (benign tumor-like growths) present in tuberous sclerosis, and a visit with a gastrointestinal specialist.

The eye doctor commented, "If she were to have tuberous sclerosis, you are in the best hands with Dr. Gomez." Other clinic staff also commented, "Oh, you have Dr. Gomez? Well, you are very lucky to have him." When the GI doctor said the same, my curious look caused him to leaf through the packet I had from neurology. He slid a tri-fold brochure from the pile and pointed to printing near the bottom that listed the author and doctor credited for discovering tuberous sclerosis: Dr. Manuel R. Gomez, Professor of Pediatric Neurology. Wide-eyed, I looked at the GI doctor surprised, "What does this mean?"

He was excited to tell the story of Dr. Gomez, "World famous for neurological discoveries, especially of tuberous sclerosis." He's an expert. You are lucky to have him."

Not only was Dr. Gomez an expert, but he was retired, returning to the clinic to help with overflow in neurology. I gulped, disappointed in myself. I was as guilty as sin for judging him based on what he looked like. It was a trait I disliked in others— and told myself earlier at the grocery store I'd never do—a narrow minded point of view of what it looks like, and therefore it must be so. Christina's earlier doctors thought that she looked fine, therefore must be. As a result they didn't trust my judgment when I said something was wrong.

I closed my eyes and scrunched my nose laughing at myself— partially in amusement, and partially in anger. Jane looked at me inquiringly. I showed her the pamphlet. She lifted her glasses that dangled from a chain around her neck and slid them on to read.

"Funny how things aren't always as they seem." I said sheepishly.

"They sure aren't," she said grinning and shook her head, "Amazing."

The third day of appointments Mathew stayed at the hotel with my friend Barb, who drove down from the twin cities while Jane and I took Christina back for final appointments.

The answer to our prayers surrounding the ketogenic diet came in the form of a tall slender dietician with short, curly brown hair named Susan Eckert.

"Since you had seen a reduction in seizure activity right from the start that is very encouraging to me." Right from the beginning, Susan was positive.

"Do you think you can help us with the diet?" I begged.

"Yes, absolutely. There are changes I want to make to the formula, and once I have those calculated, you can implement them." She never commented on the previous dietician's figures, but it was obvious they needed to be corrected.

Before leaving that day, she worked out a plan for us. We would stay in contact with her through frequent phone calls. A new formula would be implemented with solid foods to follow soon after. And, we'd monitor growth, which meant returning every three months.

"Have you seen the diet work? Has it worked for other children you've worked with?"

"Yes. It varies, but if you're asking me if the ketogenic diet works, the answer is yes. Some children have more success than others, but I believe it takes a willing parent."

Dr. Gomez had rushed into the room we were waiting in. He quickly introduced himself to Jane flipped the switch to the back-lit console on, and slid a large black film into the clip.

"Here it is, right there." He pointed. "We have found it!"

"Found it?" I blurted stunned. *There is nothing to find. What is he was talking about?*

Mournfully, I turned to Jane. She touched my arm in support as if to say, "I'm here."

She too was shocked. "We thought the MRI was normal."

His words slowed to a mild compassionate tone as he continued.

"This is not a bad diagnosis—considering the severity of seizures and what we were looking for. Look here." One hand motioned for me to come closer. As I did, a burning sensation flooded my cheeks as though a fever had set in.

"See this?" He circled a small area of the film. I looked closely and realized that this portion of the brain was whiter than others. "This is the lesion—right here. This is the right temporal lobe of her brain. You can see the lesion is about as big around as the tip of my finger." He held his pinky up and pinched the tip. "Rather small, but it goes through like a rod."

He explained that it looked like cortical dysplacia, which is a disorganization of the cortex (the outer layer of the brain where nerve cells are).

"It doesn't appear that the tubor is growing, since it hasn't *changed,*" he explained.

Shaken by the news, I tried to find words over thoughts that came quickly like, *this is permanent—final, wrong, unfair.* I had to force myself to think, thoughts were crumbling in my mind as I tried to form them. But I had to ask, "How do you know it hasn't changed?"

He lifted a different film from the large envelope, "This is the film you and your husband brought with you—from the MRI done six months earlier." He slid it under the clip.

"This film is of poor quality. However, if you look right here," using a marker, he circled a small area on the film, "you can see that it is right here on the first one, also. We have compared the two images, and they are the same size—it has not changed."

"The neurologist back home said the MRI was normal. Did they miss this?"

He looked at me and nodded, "This is not a very good image."

"How long has that been there?"

"Oh, most certainly it formed during pregnancy."

Tears appeared and words rushed out of my mouth, "Was this the cause of her seizures? If so, was she having seizures before we saw them?"

Dr. Gomez motioned for us to sit. Jane and I sat next to each other on the long cushioned bench, and he lowered himself to a round black cushioned stool and rolled closer to us.

"It's likely that she was. The area of the lesion is a large focus of seizure activity, but they are shooting all through her brain (generalized). We must get rid of the seizures!" He said clasped his hands as though we were at the beginning of a mission.

"Will she be able to think normally with this?" I asked, "Other doctors told us they didn't know and seemed less than positive when it came to her developing with the amount and type of seizures she was having." I began rambling about the amount and intensity of the seizures, mysterious diagnoses and discussions about mental retardation until he interrupted.

"Mrs. George, no matter what anyone has said, you need to treat her as a normal child."

For the first time since the storm had begun, a doctor wanted me to see hope though all the wind and rain. For months we had been hit with winds of fear, waiting to find answers. Finally, in despair, we'd given up. And now, we learned that the answer was already there. If only we'd known how to look for it. I often wondered if we had missed something, but in some ways, I'd hoped we'd never find since it might signal a deficit in mental development. But He was there—the Divine Doctor was with me, he had known it all from the beginning.

"We must get rid of the seizures! The earlier EEGs, compared to the one we just did, show there is a definite change after the ketogenic diet was introduced. I agree with you that this could be the answer for Christina."

He agreed with *me*.

"What caused this to happen?" I asked.

"There is no known cause for cortical dysplacia, if that's what this is. Remember, it only looks like that it is on our images. We cannot be sure unless we take it out and test it."

If what the image showed was cortical dysplasia and did not change, then it wasn't in itself life threatening. But the intensity and length of the seizures were. They were what we needed to conquer. During this conversation with Dr. Gomez, I realized the immunizations might have only been the trigger that had brought on an intense seizure storm.

It was all beginning to make sense. The prelude to the storm—the throwing up—quite possibly had been the outward sign of the impending storm of electrical activity shooting incorrectly in her brain. Then she was given the immunizations at a very vulnerable time, throwing her into this tornadic seizure mode.

The storm had struck with fury. This made me realize that my daughter was a sturdy, strong little girl to have survived, most likely, seizures from birth.

I began to wonder whether it was something had eaten or breathed. Like most people, I wanted to pretend that I *could* have done something, in order to feel as if I had some control—simply because I didn't. I'd forgotten, as I often did during these times, God's promise—that He would never leave me—forgotten that, ultimately, He is the one who is in control.

After the appointment with Dr. Gomez, Larry and I cried over the phone, several minutes before a long silence as we absorbed the discovery in her brain. We comforted each other, working through heavy feelings that seemed to lift as we looked past the cortical dysplasia and on to the fact that it would not take her life.

Larry's tone changed to gruff when we talked of the first MRI. We were upset not only by the doctor's behavior, but also his not reading the MRI thoroughly—the tubor missed. If it had been found and she were properly diagnosed—would the past six months of needle pokes, including the spinal tap, been needed? We were hunting for the cause, while fighting crippling fear, and all along the answer would have leaped out if the doctors had looked carefully enough.

Barb and Mathew were waiting for our return at the hotel. Putting three days of appointments behind, I knocked on the door. Barb peered through the peep hole when I arrived, and the door swung open, causing air to swoosh and her blonde, curly hair blew as if in the wind. She reached out, lifting Christina from my arms. Mathew pushed between her legs to get to me.

"Welcome back!"She smiled, surveying my face. I caught her curious gaze. Plopping Mathew on the bed across from Barb, I scrunched up next to him. Barb clasped her hands and brought them to her chin in anticipation, hoping to hear good news.

Sugar-coating, and intentionally fighting back emotion, I examined each word before it left my lips in order for my three-year-old to understand without putting fear in him.

"So the doctor found a spot on her brain and he says we need to get rid of the seizures. That is what we need to focus on. There is nothing else that could stop her from being okay." Silence engulfed us. Droplets sprang from Barb's eyes with the news of a "spot on Christina's brain" until Mathew's childlike syllables formed frankly what was on his mind.

"She's not gonna die?" His little blonde head bent upward to look at me.

Astonished at what had come out of his mouth, I stumbled for the right words. I wrapped my arms around him, and we held each other tightly.

"No, the doctor is thinking she might be okay if we can get this special diet working for her," I said, being overly optimistic.

I wondered, *How could he even know what dying meant?*

His eyes shifted to Christina in Barb's arms then back to me. His concerned face morphed into a happy, overwhelmingly joyful look as he curled his lips upward in a smile. Simultaneously, both arms extended outward as though he was going to wrap someone in a hug, then swiftly he pulled them both in toward his chest, slapping both hands smack in the middle of it, and yelled, "That's great!"

His sea green eyes glistened with happiness, and I was sure that I saw relief in them. I realized he had been there and witnessed every dreadful moment of seizure reality. Why wouldn't he think as he did? He had been present, for the most part, for every tear, every conversation laced with emotion and fear. As cute as this moment was, it seemed to tell us that he was carrying a burden and had just let it loose—sending it flying.

His childlike innocence cut right through my seriousness as our eyes locked and I smiled, trying not to blink, and pushing the tears out of my that were now-brimming in my eyes. He smiled as though he knew with all his heart, that life had taken a positive turn, and it was good.

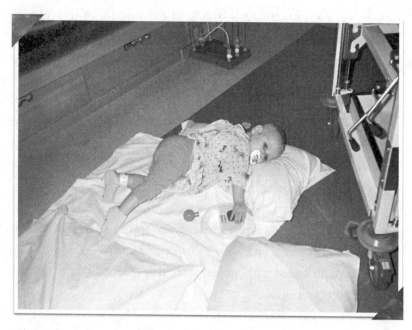

Christina, at St. Mary's Hospital, three days after we flew in to Rochester. She was too sick to move much, but her hand stayed on her musical toy.

Chapter Ten
The Fable of Failure to Thrive

"Faith is taking the first step even when you don't see the whole staircase."
—Martin Luther King, Jr.

FOG ROSE FROM THE COOLING ground and hovered over the August grass of Gruene, Texas. My cheeks felt moist to the touch, finally cooling from the heat of the day. We had spent most of the afternoon strolling in and out of eclectic shops. Whitney and I tried on t-shirts and browsed stores with shelves of clever rustic décor, Texas trinkets, antiques and homemade salsa, while Larry relaxed on a shaded bench with the two kids. When the orange sun glinted across the horizon, nearly out of sight, we headed for Gruene Hall.

After six months of hospitalizations and the long journey to Mayo Clinic in Minnesota, then back home, we finally had a break in the storm.

Within days of feeding Christina the new ketogenic formula prescribed by her new dietician Susan, the frequency and intensity of the seizures had been reduced. By the time our daughter turned thirteen months old, the seizures were gone. Life was calm.

After a month of seizure freedom our family was unfettered and free. We could go to the grocery store without abandoning our shopping cart and sprinting for the door. We could slip from the safety of our home to the nostalgic aura of Gruene without wondering if we'd have to rush home.

Fog seemed to hover and slowly dance above the grass and concrete walk as we waded through it, watching it part. When Larry pulled open the white painted screen door to Gruene Hall, the expanding spring creaking as he held it for me as I pushed the stroller in. We padded across the old wooden dance floor where Whitney and Mathew had twirled and danced wildly while a washboard musician stood atop a table several months ago. Walking past pool tables under brightly colored neon signs, a side door opened to a grassy fenced area. It was like walking into the backyard of a family reunion. People chatted while wiping messy brown barbecue sauce from their cheeks and hands. All were sitting at wooden picnic tables. Little girls ran by in fluttering, ruffled petticoats. Pursed lips of little boys blew on whirly toys perhaps just purchased at the Gruene General store. The special occasion: Saturday night barbecue at Gruene Hall.

Whitney and Mathew ran and climbed among the low branches of cedar and oak trees while I found a table and Larry bought food. A pink hat with a ruffled border framed little Christina's face as I placed the nipple of the bottle into her mouth and molded her little hands around it. She loosely held it there. As Larry made his way back from the food table, he stopped to let children run by. His strong arms, wrapped in his tan shirt with rolled-up sleeves, were balancing four paper plates of coleslaw, buns, barbecue brisket and baked beans. A neat crease flowed down the middle of each leg of his Levi jeans ending at the hem, which scrunched slightly as it rested on his black ostrich western boots.

"Kids, come on, time to eat," he yelled as he positioned the plates on the weathered wooden table. With the bottle suctioned into her mouth and gulping down formula, Christina's little eye's followed as Whitney came running, shoulder length strawberry blonde hair flying as she ran with Mathew giggling behind her.

"Whitney, wait for me!" he yelled. She stopped and waited until he almost ran ahead of her, then scooped her hands under each of his armpits and lifted him, still giggling, to his seat at the table.

Larry removed his natural straw Stetson cowboy hat and placed it upside down on the table. He steepled his hands while waiting for everyone to pay attention, then bowing his head his fingers relaxed and folded at the edge of the table. We all followed his lead.

"Lord we pray for today. Thank you that we can have this special time together, and please help Christina to get better."

Mellifluous music flowed through the crowd, mingling with the smell of barbecue and conversation—and seizure freedom. The atmosphere was festive. When a pair of young rodeo cowboys traversed by, one glanced in Whitney's direction and tipped his hat. She watched them as they walked, shiny silver and gold oversized belt buckles showing off their latest award hung on waists of Wrangler jeans with back pockets worn where the cans of skoal hid.

"Cowboys everywhere!" Whitney chided.

She reminded us of little girl afraid of boy germs. Larry and I chuckled, and she gave us a pout as if to say, "that is not funny!"

Twelve years old and not quite interested in boys, Whitney hurried to finish her meal, then jumped up and grabbed Mathew who was always ready to play. She twirled him a couple of times and ran off toward the trees to play hide and seek behind them. As they flitted off into the distance I thought about Whitney. "Only a few more years and all this innocent dislike for boys will be gone."

When a familiar song began playing, Larry slid his hat back on and took my hand. We stood up embracing in a slow dance inches from the table and from Christina, who was strapped in and resting in the stroller. Her eyes followed her daddy as he made funny faces at her while we danced. Her feet went up and her hands grabbed on to them giggling. I was in heaven.

———◆———

Christina's face was rounder and healthier, and she seemed to thrive in every way except her development. Under the advice of a neighbor who worked with the school district, I contacted Home Spun, the name of the local agency that worked under the federal disabilities act and had therapists who work with "special" children, age's birth to three.

When tested, our daughter failed 28 of 52 items from a list of cognitive, perceptual, and fine motor abilities that a one year old should be able to do. She was extremely delayed. Her finger never pointed, nor did she hold a crayon. If she wanted to pick up something, she raked it in with the open palm of her hand instead of putting her thumb and fingers together to grasp. She sat but was unstable; crawled but did not stand.

With Christina's face inches from mine, I tried to catch her eyes. I followed as she kept moving her face side to side away from mine. My lips formed dramatic smacks, and I'm quite sure if someone were watching my antics, they'd have would have laughed as I tried to entice my daughter to form a sound—any sound.

"Maammaa. Mmmaaammaaa. Mmmmaaaaa. Mmmmmmm-mmm," I would urge.

Silence.

Janet, the therapist assigned to work with Christina, often enlisted Mathew as a way of modeling something she wanted Christina to do, but when anyone tried to engage eye contact or enlist Christina to play, she turned away. There were moments when Christina did something, and it was as if we had witnessed a miracle, like when she touched Janet's short dark curly hair—contact. The contact didn't last—it never did—but we hoped and prayed with everything within us that she would begin to develop now that she was seizure free.

With each day of seizure freedom, life began to have a semblance of order again. Not perfect order, but some. Susan began introducing solid foods along with the formula and while I was learning how to become a master ketogenic chef, Whitney was about to enter sixth grade. While shopping for school clothes with her, I could tell that, to a girl approaching her teens, it was only becoming more difficult to decide what was just right.

Larry's work hours were full ten hours days, with Chet often pressuring him to stay longer. His phone, always snapped to his belt-clip, rang at all hours of the night.

"It just doesn't seem worth it, honey! He is asking too much." Staring into my husband's tired eyes, I knew he needed rest.

"Right now, we're stuck. We have mounting bills—medical bills."

Larry worried he could be fired. He was one of the top producers for the company, but knew his boss often fired people on a whim chanting, "This job isn't for everyone." Anxiety had invaded my husband's mind. He was easily frustrated and the way he held his body I could tell he was tense. I began to wonder if he should find another job.

Our kitchen became a food-lab, equipped with a gram scale to measure precisely the ketogenic food and Tupperware containers to store individual meals. We started Christina with tiny amounts of solid food. But, as we began to introduce them, Christina stopped eating.

With a tiny spoon, I tried to place mashed up beets into her mouth. She closed her lips and turned away. When I wiggled a tiny amount in, she pushed it back out as though disgusted by the food. The same thing happened with her bottle, small sips, then she pushed it away—the liquid ketogenic formula that she previously seemed to love.

We struggled to feed Christina solid, and even a partial bottle, for weeks. But when she began gagging on formula and her cheeks flushed scarlet, I knew we needed to take her to the doctor.

Neither Larry nor I felt comfortable with the pediatrician ever since the immunizations had been given. Even though he reported the onset of seizures, after immunizations with the Centers for Disease Control, we struggled with how he had failed thoroughly to investigate our concerns prior to the immunizations. Without having a new pediatrician in place, I conceded to necessity and took Christina back to him.

"I think she just has the flu, and that can take up to eleven or twelve days to pass. Bring her back if she is not better in a week," he stated reassuringly.

I wasn't reassured. Eleven or twelve days seemed like a lifetime. "She isn't eating and is getting dehydrated." I told him. But he, once again, ignored my words.

Two days later the symptoms were worse. I brought her back in hopes he would give me direction. It was a waste of time when the same generic conclusion was made. Larry and I decided to take her back to the gastro specialist she had seen in San Antonio.

When he finished examining her, his forehead wrinkled in concern. "I'm glad you brought her in. She's very dehydrated and needs to be admitted to the hospital—immediately. Admit her right now."

"What is it that is making her sick? No one else is sick in our home, and she hasn't been around anyone whom I knew was sick," I said.

"I don't know for sure, but once she's been admitted, we will take samples and do some testing. Go straight to the admitting office," he instructed again.

Before leaving, I reminded the doctor that Christina was on the ketogenic diet.

"We finally achieved seizure control. We don't want to interrupt the precious balance—she cannot have anything that is not ketogenic friendly."

He nodded and smiled, "I know the diet, and will make sure she is well taken care of."

Even though he said this, as I pushed the stroller through the skyway to the hospital—the same skyway to the hospital she had previously been in—uncomfortable feelings surfaced. The building seemed like an unfriendly, especially as I remembered the struggle here not long ago.

Larry felt the same, "How is this happening that we are taking her back there—can't we take her somewhere else?" His voice was harsh and deep. I imagined him sitting at his desk, shaking his head in disbelief.

"The doctor said that he only works out of this hospital. He assured me that they would take care of her. Larry, I'm worried. It's been weeks since she's eaten a full meal and days without drinking a bottle—I don't know how to help her."

By now, I loathed the Velcro straitjacket. From the second they put it on Christina, she began to scream, trained by then to know the pain that was to follow. Even so, she didn't resist or even flinch when the needles went in. Yet they still used the restraint. Placing the IV seemed to take forever. She was so dehydrated it was nearly impossible to insert the tube into her already collapsed veins. Three technicians and six needle pokes later, the tubes were in place.

I've heard it said that a human mother is equivalent to a lioness with her cubs. I felt it then, angry that they were even touching her. I just wanted her in my arms. After it was over and the screaming stopped, I held her, and we melted into the chair of her hospital room. An all too familiar wait for tests to come back, started again. The gastroenterologist stated, "We will know something within a day or so."

Even so, Larry was clear, "I do not want her here very long. If there is more to this than a day or two stay, I want to fly her up to Mayo. I don't care what the cost. We will borrow the money if we have to."

Christina was losing weight fast and quickly looked thin and pale, becoming lethargic. She seldom moved. She reached a critical state of dehydration that was not reversed by the IV solution.

It didn't make any sense. Since being on the ketogenic diet she had become a good eater. Why, for seemingly no reason, would she stop eating?

Twenty-four hours after being admitted—she seized, wriggling herself to a sitting position before falling over. I could hear the metal crib rattle and shake as her head fled into the mattress. Rushing to her side, I lowered the crib and lifted her face from the mattress, positioning her in my hands.

Thick tears streamed down drawn little cheeks giving way to an unnatural smile. It was a dark intense seizure that rolled in without warning.

More intense than before, her seizures came in sets or series sometimes only minutes apart—more than 100 per day.

Three days after being admitted, most of the results were back negative for any kind of infection or disease. Confused that there was nothing to treat, the head nurse sat on the floor Indian style, with Christina. She dropped droplets of formula into the little clenched mouth of Christina, but she refused to swallow.

"I don't understand why we cannot get her to eat. Have any of the test results come back in yet?" I asked.

She shook her head. "So far nothing has come back positive."

"Have you ever seen anything like this before?" I asked.

"Well, I've seen this in infants who fail to thrive," she answered.

I was afraid of even knowing what that meant, but had to ask. She explained it as a neurological condition where children give up the will to live—they stop eating—they stop surviving.

Thoughts raced: after all little Christina had been through, could she be giving up the will to live? Could my precious little one be refusing to eat <u>or</u> live? The visit with Dr. Gomez flashed in my mind; he had been positive about everything. Did we miss something?

Already mistrustful because of previous misinformation, I was not so sure what to think of this revelation. In a way, I was irritated with this nurse for so easily giving such a fateful opinion. Still, the question kept coming back to me again and again: *What about the other symptoms?*

What about the constant diaper changes and throwing up? I was fearful of what might be causing it. Could there be a genetic disorder, or a cancer, that had been missed?

When Dr. Gomez returned my phone call, I explained to him what was happening with Christina. He had already reviewed the notes from Susan but he wasn't expecting all this. "What does the doctor think she has? She must have something to make her not want food," he said simply.

I explained that they were running tests and I would call as soon as results were in. Then I told him that if she needed to be hospitalized for a longer period we wanted to fly her into Rochester and transfer care to Mayo Clinic. He seemed hesitant at first, stating that Christina could not fly until she was hydrated, it would be dangerous for her.

Since the return of the seizures, I wondered: When food isn't eaten shouldn't the body be in a state of <u>real</u> fasting. Why, then, were the ketones so low and seizures back?

"Without eating, shouldn't they be high like before?" I asked curiously.

"What—?" He paused awkwardly then spoke, "What kind of fluids are they giving her?"

I followed the tubing up to the IV bag held by the steel loop on top of the stand and read the black print: "D-e-x-t-r-o-s-e, it says dextrose,"

I heard a slight grunt and grumble through the phone, then silence. "It's too late now," he broke in disappointedly.

Dr. Gomez explained that the IV fluid given was wrong, because dextrose is sugar. It stopped the ketosis Christina was in. The seizure freedom was over, due to an unnecessary mistake. The apprehension in his voice about bringing her back to Mayo subsided.

"She needs to be hydrated before traveling here, that's first. Then I want her to eat. If she won't eat on her own, they need to tube feed her. Is that clear?" He was short and to the point. "Call me when she is ready and I will make preparations for her to be admitted."

Anger ripped through me. *Did this hospital even care?*

A flustered nurse ran to get the doctor when I pointed out the mistake. I felt as though he had let us down—let Christina down. When he arrived through sobs I told him just that and more: He didn't keep his promise about making sure the diet would be followed—even though the instructions right down to the IV fluid had been faxed over by Susan. Shaking his head in disappointment, he agreed to order the feeding tube, and left to do so.

With relentless seizures back, Larry and I again tried to balance my absence from home at the hospital with what was best for Mathew. Being away from him again seemed wrong, but I couldn't—wouldn't leave our daughter either. Begging to help, 12-year old Whitney volunteered to take care of Mathew, but wasn't quite old enough to be left alone during the numerous hours Larry worked. With the hospital's permission, Whitney and Mathew remained at the hospital—day and night. With makeshifts beds of cushions and blankets laid out on the floor of the hospital room, the two of them pretended to camp, making tents out of blankets.

When a long series of seizures began, Christina tangled herself in IV tubing as she flew down face first onto the mattress. The seizures caused her to become so tense that I couldn't easily slip her out of the tangled mess of tubing.

Whitney stood wide-eyed, with both hands over her mouth, uttering through them, "No, oh, no!" Her face and neck flamed red.

I pressed the nurses' call button, and waited for 20 minutes. If it weren't for Whitney being there, I would not have been able to unwind the tubing and lift Christina safely out of the crib. When the nurse finally came in, I unloaded frustration at the hospital that seemed to fail us. "No one here seems to care!" I reminded her about the wrong IV fluid.

"But, we needed to get her hydrated," she defensively answered. "There might be a reason she isn't eating." She didn't say the exact words the other nurse had, but I knew she meant "failure to thrive."

That night I couldn't sleep and listened to Mathew's soft breaths as he slept near Whitney on large cushioned mats and blankets on the hospital room floor. Inches away, Christina's crib sat empty. She had fallen asleep in my arms exhausted from the day's run of seizures. My mind wouldn't quiet enough to rest, *is our daughter failing to thrive—will she survive this?*

I prayed God would once again give me direction and help us to help Christina.

Thirty-six hours later, with a frustrated tone, Dr. Gomez asked why the feeding tube had not yet been placed. He was pensive and I wondered if he was angry when he said, "I'm sorry you are having trouble. But, please, give the doctor in charge this message: Feed the baby!"

By the time Larry arrived that evening I had been to the nurses' station several times pleading for a feeding tube. Finally, Larry sternly threatened going to hospital administration.

Not long after, a nurse and dietician arrived with a portable pump and equipment for tube feeding. After inserting the tube into Christina's little nose, they wheeled her to X-ray to make sure it was placed properly and finally, the dietician brought in the formula.

"After looking over the formula, I changed the ratio," she explained.

I was shocked that she changed something so important without asking.

"What—why would we change the formula?" I sparked.

Her inability to understand the diet was part of the reason we traveled 1,200 miles for help—and now she was insistent that the diet had been formulated incorrectly? I tried to think of words to say but decided to remain silent—no one was listening anyway.

My daughter had lost two-and-a-half of her twenty pounds—and was lying lethargic in her crib. I wanted nothing more than to feed her. After filling the portable pump with formula, the machine began to pass nutrition into Christina's body.

Early evening, Larry returned to the hospital looking wrung from a long day at the office and worry about Christina. He held a white envelope and without saying anything, he placed it in my hand. Then he picked up Mathew and gave him a bear hug. I looked at him curiously.

"Two tickets. One for you, one for Christina, and your flight leaves tomorrow. The flights were expensive, we couldn't afford all five tickets, so I'm driving up with Whitney and Mathew. Whitney's mom said it is okay for her to go. My brother Jim will pick you up at the airport and drive you to Rochester."

By now, I was sick of tears, but could not fight them off.

"Are you okay?" Larry inquired.

"Do you think she is going to survive this?"

"That is why you'll be on a plane tomorrow…." Overcome by emotion, he stopped.

After requesting release information, the head nurse stood outside Christina's room obviously disturbed, searching for the words, "I-I don't know if the doctor will release her."

Larry spoke matter-of-fact, "She is re-hydrated and per Dr. Gomez's instructions she is getting food via the feeding tube.

Now, we would like to transport her to a hospital that knows the diet and can give us a second opinion."

"But, we still don't know the reason she won't eat. She needs medical care until this whole thing can be figured out," the nurse objected.

Standing tall and firm, Larry folded his arms, seething and showing anger on his face. They had no right to hinder our decision to go to another hospital, *especially* after the mistake in initiating the diet and now with the mistake in IV fluid. This mistake traded seizure freedom for the violence of seizures that we had escaped.

Larry's voice rung like iron, "I'd like to meet the one who plans on stopping me."

Five days after being admitted for flu like symptoms, Christina had lost two-and-a-half pounds. Her face was thin and pale, bruises from attempts at IV's and blood draws marked her arms. A feeding tube held in place with tape ran into her nose, as we took a step of faith and headed for the elevator. I wondered if someone would try to stop us, even worried for them if they did—Larry had a look of adamancy. He was ready to take on whomever if he needed to.

My eyes burned with sleeplessness fed by anxiety, fear, and the seizures that riddled each night. What was it that was trying to take our daughter's life? Countless blood, urine, and stool samples were taken as witnessed by numerous bruises, her weight loss evident when I held her. I fought anxiousness and tears with prayer—but struggled not to fall into the pit of despair.

The nurses and doctors all had ideas of what could be causing our daughter to be wasting away, from salmonella to food poisoning to the worst of all, failure to thrive. But their theories came to nothing. We had nothing to treat—and that nothing was trying to take her life.

THE MEDICAL DESTINY OF EACH OF US AND OUR
CHILDREN IS LARGELY UP TO US.

*To think otherwise can be damaging. There is a ten-
dency when we walk into a doctor's office to want to hand
over our problem to the doctor and say, "Here it is, please
fix it." It's comfortable, it's easy, and more often than
not, it works. Just as we take comfort in deferring to them,
many doctors are unwilling to confide in us that we may
have stepped into one of Western medicine's black holes.
There are many black holes, and they are deep, and kids
with difficult-to-control seizures are in one of them.*

*So what does that mean? It means that our medi-
cal problems and our children's medical problems are precisely that—OURS. At first, that's a pretty intimidating
and perhaps a seemingly foolish concept, both to us and
to some physicians. After all, they went through years of
education. They've seen countless patients in their practices.
And then we walk into their offices with a disease we
probably don't even know how to spell. How presumptuous and perhaps foolish of us, the patients, to ask and
then pursue the hard questions, learn the side effects, get
the second opinions, do the research, and participate in the
cure—in short, to become proactive.*

*Ironically, the "side effect" of participating in our
medical destinies may not only lead to getting better
sooner. It is empowering.*

—Jim Abrahams, founder of the Charlie Foundation
to Cure Pediatric Epilepsy.

Chapter Eleven
Labor Day

"Gentlemen, I have lived a long time and am convinced that God governs in the affairs of men. If a sparrow cannot fall to the ground without His notice, is it probable that an empire can rise without His aid? I move that prayer imploring the assistance of Heaven be held every morning before we proceed to business." [turning point of success for the 1787 Constitutional Convention] —Benjamin Franklin

STREET LIGHTS ILLUMINATED THE ROADWAYS and highways, making them appear like miniature racetracks as the plane descended. Stars glittered across the clear night's sky like precious gems trading places with the lighting on land. The intercom dinged and the voice of the pilot crackled through the plane's speaker system.

"This is your captain speaking. We are beginning our descent into the Minneapolis-St. Paul International Airport. Please make sure your seatbelts are securely fastened. We look forward to flying with you again."

"Are you all right?" asked the brunette flight attendant. Her uniform scalloped her tall frame as she smiled compassionately, surveying Christina one last time.

Lifting my head off the seat back, I took a stiff breath. "Yes, we are." Before she walked away I reminded her of our earlier conversation, "Remember her when you pray."

"Oh, we won't forget her, you can be sure of that."

As the plane taxied to a stop, I applied fresh lipstick. The mirror stared back with red, bloodshot, frightened eyes. I lifted Christina into my arms, wrapping a pink and green crochet blanket around her, intentionally tucking in arms with brown, green and blue bruises.

Being careful not to pull on the feeding tube taped into her nose, I merged into the aisle of hurried passengers exiting the plane and walked until we poured into the terminal.

Amongst knots of travelers, some starred at us while others looked inquiringly, and suddenly turned away.

Jim rushed toward us, "There you are!" His wife Shari was at his side and our nephews, fifteen-year-old Seth and eight-year-old Jesse, trailed behind.

Shari brushed her blonde hair back and reached her arms out to Christina, who pressed her head snug on my shoulder, not wanting to move. Shari smiled and wiggled two fingers into a little hand. Christina moved her fingers along with her touch as if to say, "This is okay." "Uncle Barney"—as Mathew called him—tried to make Christina smile, by wrinkling his face, and mimicking the voice of Barney the purple dinosaur from a preschool show. Christina grinned and shimmied an arm from the blanket. One hand reached toward Jim's thick dark hair, but stopped. With her head snug to my shoulder, in between Jim's funny faces, her sunken eyes looked up to make sure Uncle Barney was still there.

As Jim's Dodge chiseled toward I35 that would feed into Highway 52 and Rochester, road construction routed us north, taking us past my grandparents' old home. In the dim light, the white house with black shutters looked the same. I longed to go inside, see my Grandmother, smell her cooking and "Beautiful," the perfume she always wore. I wanted to feel her hug and reassurance. I envisioned my tall grandpa behind the lawn mower, working on the rich green lawn he was so proud of. And I pictured the bouquet shaped apple trees that supplied fruit for Grandma's famous pies. My heart ached for grandma. Why did she have to leave at such a time as this? I needed her.

It was after 11 p.m. and the hallways were barren. The receptionist flipped through papers and found Christina's name. We waited until a dark-haired, male nurse arrived to escort us to the room. Jim, Shari and the boys headed back to Stillwater.

With Christina in my arms, I followed our escort through the hallway. Stopping in front of shiny steel elevator doors, he pushed the button for the third floor. "My name is Mark, I will be Christina's nurse." He smiled warmly at her.

As the elevator craned up, I wondered, *Will we find the mysterious illness?*

When the steel elevator doors drifted open, colorful and bright tile lined the walls of quiet hallways. A nurse quietly padded by in tennis shooed feet. Children's artwork—black lines showing trees, flowers and mommies and daddies, colored in with every hue imaginable by tiny hands – were cemented in rows along the walls.

"Is it always this quiet?" I asked.

"It's late, but with the holiday weekend we try not to keep anyone unless we have to."

"Holiday weekend—what holiday?" I was surprised.

Mark looked at me curiously. "Um, it's Labor Day—weekend." He looked at me curiously.

"Yes, it's just that, I didn't know what weekend it was," I replied.

"You have a good excuse. You've been a little busy lately."

The room assigned to Christina had been prepared. Bumper pads—thick bumper pads encircled the crib, and syringes of Ativan (an emergency anti-seizure medication) were set out.

Mark opened a cupboard. "Okay, let's see, diapers and wipes in here." He opened the bathroom door, showing me a tub sitting higher than usual, making it easier to bathe a baby.

"When was her last seizure?" he asked, opening a chart attached to a clipboard.

I answered questions, but was more interested in making sure he knew the diet. "Do you know that she is on the ketogenic diet? And that she cannot have sugar or anything in the IV that has sugar?"

Mark nodded, "Yes, instructions are right here." He wiggled the clipboard holding papers, "nothing is to be given unless first cleared with the dietician. That includes her IV." He lifted up a plastic bag that read SALINE in black letters. "This is what she gets tonight."

Mark assisted as I changed her into her new, clean yellow hospital gown. Threading her arms into the sleeves, the looseness of her skin bore witness to her significant weight loss.

When the capped IV would not flush, Mark called the lab to have a new one placed.

In the treatment room down the hall, I scanned the room in search of the device—the straight jacket, but didn't see one.

Two lab nurses placed syringes and open packets of alcohol wipes onto a metal tray in preparation when I asked, "Where is the Velcro jacket?"

They stopped, looked at each other, and curiously at me. "Do you mean a straitjacket?" asked one of the nurses.

I nodded slowly, feeling strange as though I had said something wrong.

Brown hair with soft lights pulled in to a pony tail, flipped to her back as she positioned herself to demonstrate how they would be holding Christina.

"We don't restrain children. The only part of Christina I need now is this portion of her arm right here." She rested one arm on Christina's forearm and used the other to hold her elbow straight.

I was tired of crying, but tears came anyway. This time they signified relief and confirmation. The straitjacket was gone. One nurse held our daughter's arm perfectly still, while the other inserted the new IV into a tiny bruised arm.

Shortly after, Christina and I went to her room. I heard a rustle from Christina's crib. I leaped from the long cushioned bench that doubled as a bed, throwing a blanket off and onto the floor. She turned, twisting the tubing from the IV and feeding tube as her head fell forward against the padding. I squeezed my arm between the bars of the crib and placed an open hand on her face, stopping the next fall. My arm didn't reach the nurses' call button. Christina was sick to her stomach, and what was a clean crib quickly became soiled with a tangled mess of tubing. Through the glass, Mark saw what was happening and swiftly came in. He pressed the nurses' call button and calmly lowered the crib side while I held Christina's head erect. Within seconds, three other nurses rushed to assist. Working together, they detached the tubing from Christina and pushed aside the tangled web. One opened the alcohol swab, and another readied the syringe.

"Not long ago we had seizure control," I whispered.

Mark counted the minutes as he spoke. "Doctors will be coming early in the morning—they will get to the bottom of this." The series ended within ten minutes later, just short of the time needed to give the emergency medication.

"Dr. Buchhalter knows she is here. You'll be seeing him in the morning."

I rigged a smile.

Mark started water in the bath. "Here, Mom, let me take her. I will wash her up." He reached for her. "You look like you need to clean up, too."

At first I didn't know how to respond. At the old hospital, I hadn't dared to leave Christina's side—that was our responsibility. I hesitated.

"It's okay. I promise to take good care of her," he said. "The parents' shower is down the hall to the left."

I looked down at my spattered shirt and realized I needed to clean up.

A grey-haired nurse hummed as she entered the room, arms loaded with towels. She handed me a towel and soap, and Mark slipped Christina from my arms.

By now fog had enveloped my mind. With a white terry cloth towel dangling over my arm, I slowly walked through the hallway realizing, I had no idea where to go. Mark had told me, but in my diminished state of thinking, I couldn't remember. I stopped and glared at the door to my left. *Was this it?* Pushing it open slightly, I peeked in. Tables and chairs faced a long blackboard—this was not the right room. As I began to creep backward something caught my eye, and I froze.

Written in white chalk on the blackboard were the words: "Room 301 Ketogenic diet ... know the protocol or do not enter!"

Three-zero-one—our daughter's room.

The board was filled with instructions on how to take care of a child on the ketogenic diet, from the type of IV fluid to medication and food. I read much of what was on the board. Then, knowing this wasn't a room for parents to be in, I backed out quietly closing the door.

Across the hall, two doors down, I found the parent's shower, the door obviously labeled. Warm water sprinkled onto my face hiding tears of relief. *They cared. The level of care is different-better.*

That night sleep was deep with the worry over seizures lessened knowing help was there watching through the glass.

Early the next morning a tall doctor stood outside the room reading the chart. A group of young doctors gathered around him. They chatted, volleyed questions, read more of the chart and discussed—it was a meeting that could have been confused with a heated debate over a controversial issue if you didn't know the reason they were there. Before entering our room, the discussion slowed and it seemed a mutual consensus was met.

The pediatrician in charge, Dr. Morgenstern, opened with questions: How long has she been like this? When did she stop eating? Has she been in contact with anyone sick?

When finished, he outlined the plan. "We would like to have new urine samples taken and sent to the lab as well as stool cultures. Blood work also needs to be done," he directed. "We will begin to rule out causes one by one."

Before 7:30 a.m., several teams of doctors had come and gone when only two stood outside reading the chart and discussing for a long while. When the dietician joined them, through the partially-opened door I heard the word "ketogenic" and realized they were from neurology.

Both were dressed in handsome, darkly colored suits. One wore a distinctive bow tie. I intentionally watched my thinking—there would be no pre-judging of doctors, this time. What I allowed was hope. Hope that the new neurologist would be our rescuer, navigating us out of the tumultuous seizures that once again were raging.

When the two doctors entered the room, I realized the distinctive bow tied doctor could be our new neurologist. His Mayo Clinic identification read, "Dr. Jeffrey Buchhalter, Department of Pediatric and Adolescent Medicine, Neurology."

"Tell me, why travel so far?" Dr. Buchhalter queried.

I recounted the past two months, which had seemed a miracle when Christina was given the proper formulation of the diet. We came here because we knew the diet was developed here.

"For some reason, this diet evaded the staff at the hospital we came from. They gave her dextrose instead of saline, and dismissed my concerns. The seizures returned."

"I understand, it's frustrating." Dr. Buchhalter nodded.

Reliving the past week, I became incensed. My tone was reflexive of that, but Dr. Buchhalter allowed me to continue and I was thankful he wasn't offended by my candidness.

From the first MRI reading that missed the lesion, to pulling her off the diet the first time, I choked on emotion mispronouncing the first deadly misdiagnosis, "non ketatonica." He pronounced it correctly for me. Obviously, he had read her chart. I realized there was nothing we could do about the pain and agony Christina had already endured, much of which should have and could have been avoided. But it could not go on anymore.

"Both my husband and I wanted her neurological care to be here. If there is something we don't understand, help us learn. We need to work together."

There was a sense of compassion from Dr. Buchhalter. It seemed that, perhaps, it wasn't the first time he heard of a story such as ours.

He thought silently for a moment, and then nodded. "Whatever is making her sick is our first priority."

Hesitating to find the right words, I almost didn't ask for fear of the answer. Is she failing to thrive?" *Surely he had seen the notes from the previous hospital.*

He shook his head dismissively. "We will find the real cause of her illness."

Our wing of St. Mary's Hospital had only two children for Labor Day weekend, our daughter and a little boy whom I guessed to be about two years old. A collage of pictures and balloons decorated his room. Nurses passed by our door pushing him in a stroller, while ushering along an IV stand. His skin was pale and yellow. His mom, juggling work and several other children at home, told me her youngest was here, waiting for a liver transplant.

There are many children suffering from critical illnesses. Knowing that it was not just us reminded me we did not suffer alone.

Scampering down the hall were footsteps, familiar footsteps and voices. I rushed to the open door just in time for Mathew to barrel into me howling, "Mommy!"

Tired and lagging from the trip, Larry's face was stubbled, but I couldn't wait to touch my lips to his or feel his face next to mine. Whitney, with a red face, hugged me but didn't speak. On the floor a cushion and several blankets were arranged for Christina to lie on. We huddled in a circle around her as she lay stomach down, still lethargic. Whatever was that was invading her body it was taking its toll. She hardly moved. She took gentle sucks on her pacifier while one arm lay outstretched touching, but not pressing, her favorite musical toy.

Larry moved about, restless from the long drive, with worry at what might be trying to take our daughter's life. When he told me he was leaving to have dinner with an old friend who was driving into Rochester, I felt deserted. Both of us were emotionally stretched and our conversation erupted into a tearful argument before he left for dinner.

At dawn, the next morning rounds were beginning. Alone, a young female pediatrician, with straight shoulder length black hair, strode into the room.

"Has anyone been here yet to tell you?" she eagerly asked.

"No. Tell me what?" I stepped back bracing for what I worried would be devastating.

Her speech was vivace. "We found the cause of Christina's illness. She has a UTI infection. We are going to begin treatment shortly. First, she will be given a fairly high dose of antibiotics through the IV. Then she will be on an antibiotic orally along with that."

Standing still, I squeezed my eyelids shut trying to understand the term UTI. It was a term I'd heard before, but didn't recall at first. My eyes flew open when I understood the inititals. I was incredulous, "A bladder infection?"

Nodding, she continued, "Babies can have a urinary tract infection and if it goes undiagnosed, it can cause severe bowel disorders. They stop eating from pain."

Pressing open palms to my temple, I stared wide-eye at the young doctor as the news became real. Five days in another hospital, then flying her up here to St. Mary's—worried for her life… for a bladder infection!

"What made you think it was a bladder infection?"

She looked down at the clipboard, and I detected a subtle smile, "We just followed up on the test results from the hospital Christina was first admitted to. It showed an increase of bacillus in the urine, so we tested further. The count is very high. She is very sick. But, we can treat this. In the meantime, we will be running other tests to ensure there are no obstructions or abnormalities. Those tests will be scheduled right away."

Any frustration at Larry washed away with relief that our daughter's illness would not be something that could take her life. When I phoned him with the news, he gathered the kids and they rushed to the hospital and we celebrated together.

The terror of the unknown and negative thinking—like failure to thrive—began to dissipate when a bag with antibiotics was hung next to the one with saline. It was an answer to our prayers.

When the pediatrician asked to remove the feeding tube my first reaction was, "No."

But Dr. Buchhalter agreed with this decision and explained, "Since the infection is being treated, she will want food. She has to do this on her own. Let's give her a chance to get hungry."

It was his prompting that caused Larry and me to agree.

Forty-eight grueling hours without food passed. We pressed the nipple to her lips filled with the correct ketogenic formula every few minutes, but she refused it.

I paced back and forth worried, wondering what course to take next when Larry's voice choked a whisper, "Paulette."

In his arms Christina's little lips moved, wrapped around the nipple. She was drinking. Tears brimmed Larry's eyes as he watched our daughter take her first sips of formula in weeks on her own.

Christina remained in St. Mary's Hospital for three more days while recovering from dehydration, a UTI infection, and malnutrition.

Even though she didn't speak, when Christina placed her hands on Mathew, he would fall to the floor—she laughed every time—they connected.

Chapter Twelve
The Prescription

"Hope is that thing with feathers that perches in the soul and sings the tune without the words and never stops...at all."–Emily Dickinson

SEPTEMBER, ONE OF THE WARMEST months in Texas, began to lose its fervor cooled by the touch of October's winds. So much had changed in our lives since that first seizure fell. Was it only a year ago that we had a "normal" life and believed in our own strength? We had fallen to our knees and cried out for help—and God answered. Now, we lived in faith, accepting the grace to withstand each terrible seizure. We waited in hope of a miracle.

Sunlight filtered through the window of Christina's room. Lightning white beams landed on a fleece blanket that I flattened against the carpet. Her toys surrounded her—soft coffee-colored bears, sweet-looking rag dolls and books with worn cardboard edges were all within reach. But, she ignored these and played with her favorite toy, a white and blue plastic toy that played music when its buttons were pressed. The toy itself resembled a hard plastic purse. Mathew crawled, on all fours. It was clear he wanted her attention because he plastered his nose against hers and screeched, "Christinina!" just long enough to distract her—and he took her toy, sliding it behind his back. It wasn't done in a malicious manner. He just wanted her to notice him. But, Christina didn't understand where her toy had gone. Her bottom lip trembled and she gathered herself to a cry. Mathew saw this and his shoulders lowered and his lips dipped down in a frown. He shot a sideways glance at me, and handed the toy back to her.

Later that afternoon Mathew received his wish. His little-boy feet padded briskly across the tile kitchen floor, he stepped into a puddle of spilt water, slipped, and went crashing to the ground on his back. As he pushed himself up uninjured—Christina, sitting in her walker nearby giggled. Thrill shone on Mathew's face, his blue eyes widened—*was she giggling at me?* Then he narrowed his eyelids calculatingly. His arms began to flail and he pitched himself forward causing a controlled, but exaggerated fall. Christina blasted out a chortle. Mathew stood up, flailed his arms above his head again and landed splat on the floor again. This time she let out a cachinnation looking directly at him. Mathew and I burst into laughter until our eyes were wet from rapt tears. It was a miraculous connection.

When Christina developed a deep raspy cough, my friend Kortnee, who was also the director of Mathew's preschool, suggested I take her to a new clinic in San Marcos. Using an otoscope to look into Christina's ear, Dr. Sue nodded. "She does have an ear infection." When she clicked her pen closed and handed me a prescription, I wouldn't take it. The liquid antibiotic she prescribed contained sugar, and we needed a ketogenic-friendly antibiotic. Ketogenic meaning: no carbs and no sugars. I asked her to call Dr. Buchhalter.

Pushing her coal black pony tail off her shoulder and evaluating me with concerning deep brown eyes she stated, "Christina needs a local neurologist."

Larry and I had prepared for this in advance. As her advocates, we had made the decision to shield our daughter from the possibility of another repeat disaster with the wrong medication or IV, and I asked Dr. Sue to please make the call.

She agreed, but when she left to make the call, I worried that she would convince Dr. Buchhalter we needed a local neurologist. But that was not the case when she returned.

Dr. Sue submitted, "He said it was okay with him if you decide to have a local neurologist, but he also said that he did not think Mom was comfortable with that. And it was *your* decision. Oh, and you were right. She cannot have what I prescribed. Dr. Buchhalter had faxed over a list of medications she can have. I will call a prescription in."

After that conversation, I knew Dr. Buchhalter was the right choice for our daughter. It cemented the trust that was needed. He had listened to Larry's and my concerns, we were being heard, and included as a vital part of our daughter's care.

Janet, Christina's therapists' jaw was tight and her body tense. Creases formed on her brow. She was concerned about one of her other patients, and she talked to me from the floor of my living room. Her curly black hair framed her face as she lay sideways. One arm braced her head. Christina wiggled her back snug against Janet.

A few weeks prior, Janet had asked if she could give my number to another mother whose daughter, just a few months younger than Christina, was having unstoppable seizures.

Janet scowled. "After she asked her doctor about the diet, he told them it was a fad."

Even though Christina was still having seizures since returning home from the hospital in Rochester, we all knew the seizure freedom she had had was due to the ketogenic diet. For another neurologist to refute the validity of the diet was troubling to me.

Christina had weekly therapy sessions with Janet, but shortly before the next scheduled appointment, Janet canceled. While talking to her, I could sense sadness and wondered if she had been crying. When we saw her the next week, her heart was heavy. That same little girl whose mother Janet had tried to share the ketogenic diet with, had a severe seizure on her first birthday and had died.

Red faced and struggling to hold back her emotions, Janet shared how difficult it was to watch a little child suffer from intractable seizures and to know there was another treatment option that might help. My heart ached for that family.

I wondered if this could have been prevented. What if the diet slowed those horrific seizures? Why didn't the neurologist even know about this diet? Wasn't that his job? Have we been so conditioned by pharmaceutical ads on TV to believe chemicals are our only hope?

Millions, maybe billions, of dollars are spent every year on ads with buff, successful-looking men who tell us, "Talk to your doctor about Medicine *X*." And there are ads with serious-looking women claiming to have found the drug solution to whatever it is with the soothing sound of synthesizers and piano arpeggios. I'm not saying there isn't a need for medicine, but we have taken that need to a whole new level by relying on it as a "fix" for almost anything.

We will never know if this little child so close to our Christina's age would have benefitted from the ketogenic diet. What we do know, is that the diet was not given as an option. And, even if it was, the doctor whom the family depends on would need to give an accurate account about the ketogenic diet in order for the child to benefit from it.

I understood Janet's pain. We had seen the ketogenic diet help Christina. But the heartbreaking reality was that some children with intractable seizures—weren't allowed the gift of this diet. It ignited a desire within me to change that.

The extra room in our home doubled as Whitney's weekend bedroom and my office. There, I kept files of medical paperwork, scads of notes, and ketogenic menus. Larry purchased a computer system for the office to help with researching epilepsy and treatments.

While Susan and I worked on "tweaking" the diet by adding and changing foods by day, after the kids were asleep at night, I searched the Internet.

It wasn't long before I found a ketogenic mailing list. In dim light, the computer screen glowed, illuminating my face and sometimes my emotions that unleashed from reading posts from brokenhearted parents who seemed to pullulate by the day. Parents from all walks of life, logged on in hope. They were from all over the world. At times some of the e-mails were overwhelming. Parent's cried out in anguish at not finding relief from seizures, their children's lives in danger.

Their stories were our story. We felt the same pain. We had the same fears, and were in the midst of the same tempest storm.

Out of thousands of posts and hundreds of parents on the list, one name kept reappearing in my inbox: Diane. Her daughter Mandy became seizure-free on the ketogenic diet. After two years of being seizure-free, the diet was removed. Now, Mandy was seizure free, in school, and doing fine. Diane believed the ketogenic diet had saved Mandy's life.

Diane wrote, "I can't believe how similar Mandy's and Christina's stories are." Mandy was older than Christina when the seizures had begun, but their stories were strikingly similar. Diane's encouragement meant so much to me. Hope was easier to hang on to knowing there was another child who had become seizure-free on the ketogenic diet.

After emailing her about an upcoming appointment at Mayo Clinic, Diane wrote: "Mayo Clinic—Dr. Buchhalter! He was Mandy's doctor! He moved from Oregon to practice at Mayo."

Considering we lived in Texas and Diane and her family lived in Oregon, it never occurred to us that our daughters could have the same neurologist—it was an astonishing revelation.

There was no doubt in my mind prior to this e-mail Dr. Buchhalter was the doctor Christina was supposed to have. This Internet coincidence confirmed that he was the ketogenic expert we needed.

While reading some of the posts, I realized most people thought of the ketogenic diet as only that—a diet—without knowing its history or why it was developed. I wondered if the point was being missed.

Remembering the scripture verses that were listed on "The Ketogenic Diet Information Sheet," I opened my Bible and flipped to Mark 9:18-29 (ESV):

And someone from the crowd answered him, "Teacher, I brought my son to you, for he has a spirit that makes him mute. 18 And whenever it **seizes** him, it throws him down, and he foams and grinds his teeth and becomes rigid. So I asked your disciples to cast it out, and they were not able." 19 And he answered them, "O faithless generation, how long am I to be with you? How long am I to bear with you? Bring him to me." 21 And Jesus asked his father, "How long has this been happening to him?" And he said, "From **childhood**. 22 And it has often cast him into fire and into water, to destroy him. But if you can do anything, have compassion on us and help us." 23 And Jesus said to him, "'If you can'! All things are possible for one who believes." 24 Immediately the father of the child cried out [some manuscripts add tears] and said, "**I believe; help my unbelief!**" 25 And when Jesus saw that a crowd came running together, he rebuked the unclean spirit, saying to it, "You mute and deaf spirit, I command you, come out of him and never enter him again." 27 But Jesus took him by the hand and lifted him up, and he arose. 28 And when he had entered the house, his disciples asked him privately,

"Why could we not cast it out?"[or heal him] 29 And he said to them, "This kind cannot be driven out by anything but **prayer**." [some manuscripts add fasting] (emphasis mine).

I marveled, "seizures—the boy in the story had seizures! Jesus knew what a seizure was." I'm not sure why that pressed upon my heart strings like it did, because I knew in my head that Jesus had healed everyone who came to Him. What I didn't realize was this account that Mark had written about, some 2,000 years previous, would mirror us.

The Inspirational Study Bible says, "Imagine the pain of the father in the story. While other parents could watch their children grown and mature, he could only watch his suffer. While others were teaching their sons an occupation, he was just trying to keep his son alive."

We identified with that father!

Larry and I and the members on the ketogenic mailing list, we're just like him. We were a people desperately seeking help while watching our children's lives being overtaken by relentless seizures. Those seizures were weathering away our children's precious days of development.

After reading this biblical story, I learned that this healing we were seeking required prayer. Fasting was only part of the prescription. In the ESV study Bible commentary, it states this in regard to the disciple's inability to heal the boy: "Their failure is an occasion for encouragement of more prayer implying that more time and effort in prayer leads to growth in faith."

As hard as it was to envision a seizure free Christina, running, playing and talking, I had the stories of Mandy and the boy in scripture healed by Jesus to help me hang on to hope. I knew that in my weakness of hope, **He is strong**, and mustard seed faith **could** move a mountain (emphasis mine).

Christina on the beach in Corpus Christie.
She was walking—and falling—but she walked

Chapter Thirteen
To Achieve the Impossible

"I know God will not give me anything I can't handle. I just wish that He didn't trust me so much."—Mother Theresa

NINE MONTHS LATER WE STOLE away for a vacation.

Just off the coast of Corpus Christie Bay our hotel reclined in sun-drenched sand. The serene, sapphire blue Gulf of Mexico that flowed into the bay had brought us here for a much needed weekend getaway—our last one in Texas.

Larry and I had come to this same beach many years before. I flashed back to those carefree days before kids. Sunset walks on Padre Island were sensuous memories of our vernal romance. Back then we were planning our future—a future without seizures. Love had changed since giving birth to Mathew and Christina. Now, it was a fuller, un-superficial, and deep love expanded to the kids. With its richness, I realized that I never knew what true love was until I met Larry and had our children.

The ocean tide spread across the sandy beach. Christina, a month shy of two years old, was a silhouette against the bright waters. Her pink hat stirred in the wind and she watched the ocean waves rolling against the shore. Since the soft sand cushioned her falls, we allowed her to roam freely. Her little legs, still novice at walking, toddled to outrun a thin sheet of water pouring onto shore. She smiled in delight, as if this was a game—between her and the ocean—running after the water as it receded back into the Gulf, dropping shells on the sand. Her joints were "loose" and she fell often since taking that first step, holding onto a cupboard door, at eighteen-months-old.

Mathew sat near Christina at the edge of the pressing and pulling waves. He squished his legs and wiggled them around, making long indentations in the moist sand which filled with water and smoothed with sand as the bay washed in. He giggled with pleasure as he waited for the next wave to wash over him.

Dinnertime approached and we gathered our family and headed toward the restaurant. Seagulls croaked and cried above us, no doubt asking for food. Larry and I walked hand in hand along the shoreline, letting the warm water lap against our feet, before turning to cross the parking lot toward the restaurant. Christina fussed when Larry picked her up. She didn't want to be restrained, but we worried that she might have a seizure on the hard pavement.

Since she was hospitalized last fall and given dextrose in the IV instead of saline, we still could not get Christina seizure-free. We (the kids and I) had been back to Mayo Clinic three times for follow-ups, blood work, and weight and height measurements. Susan "tweaked" the diet several times in an attempt to find that perfect balance we had once had. Although we managed to see a decrease in the amount and intensity of the seizures, they still came randomly. I fought off anger at the IV mistake every day.

Return visits to Mayo Clinic took place every three months for blood work and EEG's. Each time, Dr. Buchhalter carefully examined the CBC (complete blood count) report to make sure Christina was getting the proper nutrients. Whenever he changed the ratio (ratio meaning percent of fat to protein and carbohydrates) of the diet, he included Larry and me in the decision making. I was thankful for Dr. Buchhalter's willingness to work with us, and even more grateful for his determination with the ketogenic diet.

Here in Corpus Christie, the restaurant's screened windows provided no relief from the warm, humid air. The host guided us through the dimly lit room, weaving his way around tables of chattering, shorts-and-tan clientele. Smiles and conversation rose through the air. The restaurant was happy. This was vacation.

Our table was near a rectangular speaker that projected the artistic wanderings of a one man band. Mathew was fascinated. The man, dressed in a loose, flowery shirt, sang songs from the seventies and eighties. He turned comedian and offered lame—and, in the context of a vacation—hilarious jokes. At one point, he saw Mathew sitting on the edge of his chair, staring at the stage attentively. The man's eyes narrowed and a grin slipped across his face. He covered the microphone with his hand and said, "Help me, help me—I'm in the speaker." The muffled voice confused Mathew and he slid off his chair to investigate the speaker more closely. After careful study, he shook his head, looked at the man on the stage—and pointed in an accusatory manner. Laughter sprung up across the restaurant, but Larry seemed distracted.

Larry's short trim beard etched his jaw line. His brown wind-blown hair bordered tenseness in his face. He had been quiet, unusually quiet since before we left home.

"Is everything alright?" I wondered if he needed to tell me something.

"As long as I give two weeks' notice right after commissions are paid, the only money we'll lose will be commissions from the next month," he blurted.

Larry's job the past few months had been horrible. Drivers called throughout the night and at times, so did Chet. One night as we huddled on the couch, Chet called. He demanded that

Larry come to the office—on a Saturday night. Worried that he might lose his job and our insurance, Larry reluctantly obliged.

Adding to the stress, Christina still wasn't seizure-free. She didn't speak, point, hold a spoon, and seldom made eye contact. Since return visits to Mayo Clinic were required every few months, we began to wonder if we needed to move.

When a company in Wisconsin offered Larry a job and sent him a salary proposal, he poured over numbers for days. The new job paid less than what he was making and insurance was out of network, but he thought we could make it work. The office he would work out of was in Illinois, six hours from Mayo Clinic— less than a day's drive.

St. Francis of Assisi once wrote, "Start by doing what's necessary; then do what's possible; and suddenly you are doing the impossible."

Between the uncertainty at his work and the inability to gain seizure control, we knew we had to do something. It was clear that the best chance our daughter had was the ketogenic diet. We had done all that was necessary, we evaluated what was possible, and decided we needed to move to do what's possible, to try and achieve the impossible.

Larry accepted the job offer.

In between bites of steak and salad, I spoon fed Christina bits of chicken and beets and whipping cream (her ketogenic meal) while Larry and I gathered thoughts about the future. Since he was worried commission might be withheld, he wanted to protect us from a financial crisis and plan accordingly. Larry decided not to give more than the required two weeks' notice. And when we placed our home on the market, we did not allow the realtor to put a sign in the front yard in case someone from work drove by. When our house sold, we planned to tell Whitney. Since it usually took a couple of months to close on a home, we figured we would have at least that much time left to spend with her. Both

Larry and I agreed not to discuss our plans while he was at work, and we promised not to tell anyone until it was safe to do so.

This weekend trip to Corpus wasn't just a vacation; it was our way of taking in what we could of the Texas I had grown to love.

———◄▪►———

It wasn't long after we returned home from our trip that our carefully thought out plans to protect our family fell suddenly apart.

Larry had left for work. I half dozed back to sleep but awakened to footsteps coming down the sidewalk to our home. *Who in the world would be coming to our front door this early?* I thought. Reaching up to the nightstand, I turned the clock so I could read the time: 7:20 a.m. It was too early for the realtor to show the house—then I heard the key turning in the lock and leaped out of bed. "Who is it?" I called, peeking toward the front entry from the hallway. For a moment, I worried that someone was breaking in, but had no time to think before the door wheeled open and Larry's boots clicked, softly, on the tile entryway.

Larry's eyes traveled the distance from the ground to my face.

"He fired me," Larry said, his shoulders, normally square, were round and fallen.

My mind skipped. Larry was a conscientious worker. He took his job seriously. There was no way that he was fired because of poor performance. Larry brought in a lot of money for the company. I was unable to form anything but the simplest of questions, "Why?"

"He was suspicious we might want to take Christina up North for medical care. After work he'd been going through my computer and my e-mails. He found one that you forwarded to me from Dr. Buchhalter reminding you to call as soon as we arrived in Illinois."

Our fears were confirmed, but neither of us anticipated what came next.

Larry continued, his face wrought with anger, "He copied the e-mail and put a copy on everyone's desk—his way of justifying my being fired."

"But in that email I listed my concerns about her development and the seizures!" I folded my arms at the waist and bent over letting out a curdling sound of disgust. Chet had invaded our children's privacy. He had stepped on what I considered sacred ground.

Both our eyes filled with tears. We knew what the ramification of this meant; commissions lost, whether it was legal or not. We both also knew that in order to survive financially, Larry would have to leave Texas and begin work in Illinois soon.

Searching my husband's eyes, I knew there was more. His odd silence during our trip to Corpus lingered and I begged him to tell me what it was.

Larry began slowly, "One of the drivers figured out we were moving—I told him my car was for sale. He told Chet." Larry paused, knowing I would be disappointed with what he was about to say, "Chet confronted me the day before we left for Corpus. I told him I was just selling my car—but I figured he would dig further—I knew this might be coming."

Now it was clear to me why he was so distant at the restaurant in Corpus. As he explained, his words together became more like an elegy. I mourned over the agreement we had made, not to say anything to anyone—an agreement he did not keep. However, I couldn't blame him alone. I had a part in this too by sending the email.

For both of us, the seriousness of life the past two years and the effort and pressure involved was difficult beyond words. There were times neither of us knew what to do. The financial strain of trips back and forth to Mayo Clinic and medications not covered by our insurance had taken their toll on our savings. The formula that we had been purchasing cost four-hundred dollars every few weeks and our request for insurance to cover it had been denied.

Larry was worried for our finances, for our ability to move, and to be able to take care of our two children. We were caught in the middle of a storm of emotions and worry, being tossed about, while the meter was running on our child's development.

We worked through this drama, and I quickly forgave him and he forgave me.

Within weeks of pressing our feet into the sandy beach of Corpus Christie and feeling the warmth of the gulf's breeze on our skin, Larry left for Illinois.

Our family at the hotel on our way home
from a trip to Mayo Clinic

Chapter Fourteen
Autism the Six-Letter-Word

When you come to the edge of all the light you know, and are about to step off into the darkness of the unknown, faith is knowing one of two things will happen: There will be something solid to stand on, or you will be taught how to fly.—Barbara J. Winter

EMPTY, OPEN CARDBOARD BOXES GAPED at me, their tops folded open in a perpetual wave. Beige pieces of packing paper, flat and smooth, rested next to the boxes. The plaster walls had silver nails sticking out where baby and toddler pictures had hung. The first picture I grabbed was Christina's seven-month-old photo. Her blue eyes were piercing. I hardly noticed that they were peaking out of a white, fur blanket. I pulled another picture from an angled nail. It showed Christina at Mathew's preschool, robbed of her brilliant blue eyes, with sunken cheeks and dull countenance. My heart ached—this was taken just after the car seizure. The seizures had taken her health and vibrancy.

As much as I didn't want to leave this beautiful town and our beautiful home—and our beautiful Whitney, I knew we had to. We had to give Christina the best chance to survive—we had to stop the seizures. With that in mind, it didn't matter where we lived, or if we even had our own home. We could rent, live anywhere, and give up anything— to get her better.

Larry had travelled to Illinois to start his new job—which added a sorrowful element to this beautiful Texas day. The kids and I enjoyed snacks on a blanket that rested in our front yard. The grass, thick and dark green, tickled our feet. White puffs of gardenia blooms emitted a sweet smelling perfume near our front door, and the crepe myrtle tree's pink and ivory flowers announced summer's arrival. Mathew's hair was translucent in the sun—he was frozen, watching a monarch butterfly jump through the air and braze the tip of his nose. I crept close to him and saw his eyes cross as he tried to see the orange and black wings that were so close to him.

Before I could return to Christina, just a few feet away on the blanket, she screamed with a shrill that cut through the quiet of the morning air. Her arms thrashed and air constricted by the intensity of her pain. I rushed to her. When she caught her breath, I looked under her clothing for a bite mark, especially worried a scorpion had bit her—but could not find her pain. When her cries dwindled to whimpers, I lifted her into my arms, and carried her, then Mathew, into the house.

Later that night, alone while Larry slept in a different bed in Illinois, I laid awake. Sleep didn't come as easily for me with him gone, but after today, when Christina cried and I had no idea why, I feared her silence. Her inability to communicate worried me and thrashed in my mind.

Communication was limited to a smile or a cry, or a close-fisted attempt to grab something. Weeks earlier, Janet had given me a book on sign language. Her hope was to begin teaching Christina sign language. I declined the invitation. I felt that teaching her this way to communicate was like giving up on her.

That night, lying wide awake alone, my mind drifted toward Christina and her screams that afternoon. I wished that she could tell me what was wrong and, as if in response, a quip I'd heard flickered like a light bulb into my head, "There are a lot of things we don't know, but there are also a lot of things we do know, that we never use."

Scrunching the feather pillow, I plopped my head down frustrated at myself.

"What was I thinking?"

I'd somehow convinced myself that teaching Christina sign language was giving up. But I now realized that wasn't the case. I knew that we could teach her a way of communicating—but I didn't make use of it. And as her advocate, I needed to help her, even if it meant abandoning my own bias.

During the next therapy session with Janet, she began teaching us sign language. With her fingers together, Janet modeled the sign for "more." Placing the tips of each finger to the thumb of each hand, she then brought her two hands together midline, saying, "More? Christina, do you want more?" While I slowly plunged a spoonful of ketogenic custard into Christina's mouth, she ate but ignored Janet's instruction. The session wasn't wasted though. Mathew and I carefully watched and formed the sign for "more." Before long Janet had taught us the simple ones, "more, eat, drink, no, yes, please," and our favorite, "I love you."

At the last therapy session we had with Janet before we moved, Christina still had not shown any understanding of the signs we were using. But Janet encouraged us to continue using them each time we spoke any of the words we knew signs for—even if it didn't seem Christina understood.

Walking through the house one last time, my gaze lingered on the angles in our ceiling design and the rounded edges on the corners of the walls. We had worked with the builder to design this home two years previous and now, such a short time later it seemed, we were leaving it. I would miss our home with the personal touches, and Texas, but our friends—I would miss them all the more.

Here, so many people had become our friends, and many had offered to help and prayed for us. There were times that Sharon and I had sat cross legged on her living room carpet, sipping coffee, and tearfully talking over Christina's illness. We prayed for her healing and believed that with God, all things were possible. Our neighbors, Larry and Sue, served us Thanksgiving dinner during a time when Christina's seizures had taken their toll and I was too exhausted and emotional to cook. Kortnee had helped bring Mathew back and forth to pre-school when I was with Christina in the hospital. And Whitney and her mom were relationships we hadn't envisioned ever being far from. This house—and Texas—had become a warm, wonderful place for us. Here, I had changed my way of thinking and my faith had been tested.

The warmth here, from friendships to decorating to cooking, all so distinctly Texan, will be missed. But as the van rumbled down our street one last time, I chose to take it all with me, inside.

Just minutes from Larry's new office, we were able to rent an old farmhouse in the middle of sixty acres of farmland. With the exception of some clothing, beds, and Christina's crib, most of our belongings remained in boxes. Larry worked diligently to make enough commissions to keep our family afloat financially.

The farmhouse was quaint but weathered from age, and insects of all kinds made their way in through cracks and crevices of old rotting wood while the empty house waited for renters. Exhausted from travel, after the kids were tucked in, I curled up on the floor in anguish—overtaken by panic.

I wanted to go back to our clean house. *What were we thinking? This is awful—so much work. I can't do this.* Remembering the goal, I began to chant it, "We can live anywhere—give up anything—to get her better. We are here to be closer to Mayo. This will work."

Larry nodded in agreement, bending down as my tears fell onto the yellowed, speckled linoleum floor. He bent down and pulled me close. "It's going to work. It will be okay. Things have not been easy for me either. We'll get through it."

We mobilized and stepped arm in arm up long narrow stairs to the bedroom. The frame and mattress of our bed was assembled, and I took comfort in the smell of our own clean sheets.

Within weeks of arriving in Illinois, appointments were scheduled at Mayo Clinic. This trip was different: The last follow-up visits, I had traveled from Texas—a two day drive with two kids by myself. Since Larry could not have time off at his previous job, it was the only way we could manage it. But now, the drive was done in a day, and Larry was with us to help juggle the kids. His new boss not only allowed him to go, but even encouraged him to.

As we entered the towering grey building with the familiar bronze sculpture of a man with up stretched arms, I was thankful. Thankful for Larry being with us, and thankful we were here. The focus was now on helping our daughter become seizure-free again.

By now the doormen knew us. As soon as we entered, they pulled out a red double stroller, shaped like a two-seater car for Mathew and Christina. As we pushed the red car through the subway level, listening to its uneven wheels rattle against the tile floors, we looked at the stores that lined the hallways. It was amazing—like a mini-mall inside, stores that sold jewelry and fur and toys. It amazed me that such touristy stores were here, in a place where the main focus was on health care. But, as we traveled through the buildings, it was evident that many Mayo Clinic patrons came from all over the world. Even clothing was different. Some women wore silk flowing garments with colorful tunics. A group of women, huddled in a circle talking, wore long black

Islamic tunics and dress, their head covered in hijabs. Diverse dia-
logues mixed amongst the people as we walked the subway level.

After blood work and an EEG had been done, we headed to
east 9 to meet with Dr. Buchhalter. He wrinkled his brow as he
studied the EEG readings. His distinctive brown bow-tie sat neatly
at the neck of a white linen shirt matching his dark brown suit.

He cleared his throat then began, "There are frequent sharp
waves over the left, right, and parietal regions of Christina's brain."

He carefully explained what the images meant. The seizure
activity had increased. He carefully explained our options:

-Make no further changes and allow her to have daily seizures

-Continue to alter the diet

-Consider adding different anticonvulsant medication

-Add carnitine to assist the diet

-Consider surgery, but only after a SPECT (single-photon emis-
sion computerized tomography) scan done alongside an EEG.

Throughout this whole ordeal, we were trying to make the
best decisions possible for our daughter. Having a neurologist
work with us, who gave us all of the options, without leaving
any of them out, was empowering. It allowed us to make *informed*
decisions *together.*

The first neurologist never shared with us the ketogenic diet
as a treatment option. When we did find out about the diet, he
told us it was not safe for an infant, which is incorrect information. Considering that the diet has been around since the 1920's, I
wondered why he knew so little about it. Through research, I had
learned that since the discovery of anti-seizure medications in the
1950's, the diet's use had diminished—could this be the reason?

From the beginning, we should have been told all of the treatment options, not just the ones preferred by a particular doctor.
We needed complete and accurate information so we could make
informed decisions. Thankfully, now we could.

Allowing the seizures to continue was not an option, and neither was surgery or medications. More drugs seemed futile, and the statistics on any working after the first trial failed, was low. After discussing the four options, we agreed to continue working with the ketogenic diet, but we would add carnitine as a supplement to help boost the diet.

Near the end of our appointment, Dr. Buchhalter looked concerned when he queried about her development. He noticed as we had, that she didn't look anyone in the eyes, and her attention was usually fixed on her musical toy. Her silence, in even trying to form words, was obvious, and even though we tried each day to show her sign language, she did not seem to understand. Dr. Buchhalter recommended that Christina be evaluated by Dr. Frederick, a neuropsychiatrist.

We returned with Christina a few weeks later for psychometric testing. Dr. Frederick was a tall, thin man with curly dark hair and a face that one immediately trusts. When he smiled, we had hope. His caring demeanor emanated as he screened our daughter. Larry and I liked him right away. The developmental testing took several hours and when it was finished, Dr. Frederick told us we would have results in a week.

Both Larry and I knew that Christina had not been developing like most other kids, but nothing prepared us for what came in the mail a week later.

Using a butter knife as a makeshift letter opener, I slit the top of the large manila envelope open and slid out the psychometric test results and a cover letter from Dr. Frederick.

Some of the medical terminology evaded me, but the test results page was clear. At nearly two-and-a-half years old, Christina had tested at five-to-nine months for cognitive ability. She was seventeen to twenty months *behind* in cognitive ability.

Tears welled in my eyes. I tried to prevent them, but I could not—they splashed against the page, blurring the ink, blurring my sight. "Autism rating scale: severe to moderate," the page told me in its stark tone. "Autism."

My friend Kathe Wunnenburg wrote in her book, *Grieving the Loss of a Loved One*: "When too much pressure is put on the heart, tears are its safety valve. No matter how hard we try to control ourselves, sometimes there's just no stopping them. Though we may try to sandbag our emotions, sooner or later the wall breaks, and the tears come flooding through."

As sick as I was of tears and crying, the wall broke and the tears flowed down my cheeks and chin. We hadn't lost a loved one, but the autism diagnosis felt as much of a painful loss as anything I had ever felt.

It was too much. My heart was in a state of hurt and anguish. So much so, that I couldn't bring myself to the computer any more to post comments to the ketogenic mailing list or read posts. Previously, I'd been on the list to try and support others who were looking for help for their child. I didn't feel like I could help anyone with anything. I disappeared from the list, into my own dark pain.

Our daughter's life was being ripped away before it had begun.

I counted back to when she had the seizure-free month— more than a year ago now.

On paper things seemed hopeless. The discouraging evidence lay in front of me on tear stained paper listing my new most hated word, *autism*.

Chapter Fifteen
The Prayer that Changed Everything

Ninety-nine percent of who you are is invisible and untouchable
—R. Buchminster Fuller

"CHIN UP! MANDY AND CHRISTINA are so much alike! If Mandy can come through this, so can Christina. Remember, she has the best doctor! Don't give up!" read the most recent email from Diane.

During times when I felt as though all was lost and hope dissolute, God provided Diane. I was broken hearted over the autism diagnosis and she became an extra hand, helping me to hold on to that slippery rope called hope. She had watched her daughter suffer from seizures, felt the same hollow pain at not being able to stop them, and she had danced in the rain.

Mandy's victory over seizures inspired me to hope for our daughter and wonder what it might be like for our Christina. Would she one day make eye contact with those baby blues? What would her voice sound like if she spoke? What might it be like for Mathew to be able to play with her?

Not long after moving to the farmhouse, tassels on top of tall corn stalks stirred in the breeze. Through the window, rows of corn rounded the distant hill and faded into the blue of the sky.

In the distance, a tractor lurched through the parted rows harvesting corn. Fresh Midwestern air pressed its way through the torn screen window of our now clean and orderly rental.

I slumped onto the living room couch with my morning coffee, hugging it with both hands. On his tiptoes, Mathew looked out the window letting the breeze sweep his face as he watched the tractor until it went out of his view, then he sprinted up the steep stairway and into the playroom.

Insurance claims, stacked neatly in piles on my desk, seemed to be waiting for me. I glowered at them and sighed, it was a daunting task of rejections and partially paid claims—a foot deep. When either Larry or I called the insurance company about unpaid amounts, they would route us to the doctor's billing office, which would send us back to the insurance company. Different doctors billed separate from the hospital and it was a confusing process.

This fall morning, Christina was full of energy and angst rushing about. She partially crawled with her bottom up in the air, and partially walked. Her open handed shoves at the pressurized safety gate let me know that she didn't want to stay in the soft carpeted room we were in. Distracted by her anxiousness, I set aside tending to the insurance pile to follow behind as she let out energy.

Whenever she wandered off soft carpeting, we would follow, allowing her some space, but staying close in case of a seizure. Today, she scampered into the kitchen and ransacked a cupboard, sending tupperware bowls and covers out to the floor. She careened past the dining room and through the study. I wasn't far behind, but her little legs and arms maneuvered with fortitude as she rounded the stairs and began to climb. She padded up the stairs, her steps making no impression in flattened, gold carpet. I smiled at her agility that wasn't there before.

Her short little legs pushed up to the summit of the stairs—and she stopped. At first I assumed she was listening for Mathew. But her back stiffened. Her body fell sideways, and her head hit a stair as she began falling down the tall vertiginous steps. I lunged up the steps.

"No, no, stop!" Her body sagged and then flopped, lifeless, down the stairs, hitting each stair. I screamed, reaching my arms as far as they would extend, but it was no use—I was too far. Her arm moved and she shrieked—but went limp again as the seizure took control. My fingertips reached her and she rolled into my arms. With her legs dangling, I rushed to the kitchen for an ice pack and then to the nearest phone. By the time I reached a chair, my legs were rubbery and unstable. As I scanned her head for serious injury, her eyes popped open, and she took a deep breath in. She started to sob, until another seizure took over and she lost consciousness. I held her, unable to catch my breath as a barrage of emotions, guilt, and shock pounded through my thoughts. "I was too far away from her. It is my fault—I hate seizures!"

I cried out-loud, "Father, please help me help her!"

When the seizure series stopped, Christina laid whimpering in my arms through ragged breath while sucking her pacifier. I held an ice pack on her head.

Larry was an hour away in Wisconsin, working at the company's home office. I dialed him anyway. He helped me settle down enough to call Dr. Buchhalter.

When the nurse on east 9 told me he was in with patients, I pleaded, "My daughter is having more seizures. Please, I need him now."

When he came to the phone I explained, through hiccups of tears, what had just happened. "We have to do something. Can we change the diet?"

"Perhaps we should stop the diet and try other options—" he began, but I interrupted.

"No," I mourned, "It worked once."

His voice grew serious, "In the meantime, she needs to wear a helmet to avoid another head injury when she falls with a seizure."

Now that she was more mobile, I knew we had to do something to protect her when she was off soft carpeted areas, but I did
not want to give up on the diet.

"I know, but we have to stop the seizures." I begged choking
down sobs.

"I agree we need to do something." Dr. Buchhalter replied.

I knew he had just come out of a room with another patient
that needed him and my voice was frantic and irrational sounding.
I was sure he thought I'd lost it.

But after a moment of silence he continued compassionately,
"Let me pull her file and look things over. I will call you back."

Christina sagged on my lap, a drop of condensation from the
ice trickling down her bruised forehead, where the blue rested
next to red from the rug burns.

I felt tense and unnerved. What do I do now? Do we give up—
stop the diet? Do we fight? I was exhausted. I prayed for guidance.
But angry thoughts crossed my mind. We were nothing special, who
was I to ask for healing? Larry and I argued more now than ever
about little things—we were far from perfect. But then I remembered the bathroom floor in the hospital in Texas, and this was not
about me—and God was here, in Illinois too. I had to remember
what I knew to be true, that my belief in the cross wiped away my
sin and His grace was more than enough to cover my inadequacies. I
didn't need to be perfect. God just wanted me to trust Him.

Brennan Manning writes it this way in his book, *The Raga-
muffin Gospel.*

> When I get honest, I admit I am a bundle of paradoxes.
> I believe and I doubt, I hope and get discouraged, I
> love and I hate, I feel bad about feeling good, I feel
> guilty about not feeling guilty. I am trusting and sus-
> picious. I am honest and I still play games. To live by
> grace means to acknowledge my whole life story, the

light side and the dark. In admitting my shadow side,
I learn who I am and what God's grace means...As
Thomas Meron put it, "A saint is not someone who is
good but who experiences the goodness of God."

In the now post-ictal state, Christina lay calm and quiet on
my lap. I too was silent as I waited for Dr. Buchhalter to call
back. Words kept repeating in my head, like the skip on a record
that causes the same lyric to repeat. "Wherever two or three are
gathered—there I am in the midst of them." It repeated until I
answered my own thoughts—out loud.

"I need someone to pray with me."

In the middle of sixty acres of corn, in a farmhouse in an area
of Illinois I didn't even know existed until a few months ago, it
came to me, clearly. I remembered the story when Jesus spoke
these words. He was affirming this to His disciples that He would
be divinely with them. There was power in their agreement with
him in their midst. Born out of desperation, came the solution
that brought this verse to life in our home.

"Mathew?" I called, but no answer. I summoned again, "Mathew?
Say, here I am." This phrase we began saying after he had walked
away from me in a shoe store in Texas. Larry and I engraved in his
mind that if either of us called, "here I am," he was to answer.

The steps creaked as his bare feet patted down. "Here I am,"
he called.

Wiping the remnants of tears from my face, I cleared my throat.

"What?" he said standing in front of me, surveying my face.

"You know that Christina's been sick, right?" I asked.

He nodded his head yes, looking sad.

"You also know that Jesus died for our sins, right?" I asked him.

He again nodded yes.

"Would you pray with me right now, and agree with me for
Christina to get better?" I asked.

His face lit up, and his hair flipped back and forth as he nodded his head with an enthusiasm to be envied.

I took his hand and rested it on Christina along with mine. He bowed his head, and squeezed his eyes shut. He was serious as I began to pray. I wanted to pray with a clean heart and asked first for forgiveness. Among my personal list of shortcomings was anger: anger at the hospital in Texas and anger at Larry's former employer, and my less than kind attitude toward people in our lives who implied we needed to accept things the way they were. I didn't have to like what they said or what happened, but hanging onto hurt wasn't right either. I let it go.

"Lord, I'm lost, and need your help." My young son and I agreed together for Christina's healing. "Lord, we thank you that you are with us. Please, stop the seizures, heal Christina. We pray for her doctor to have wisdom, and we pray for us to stand strong through this."

Mathew's eyes squeezed shut and his fingers wrapped tight on my hand. When the prayer was finished, he said, "Amen!" then pranced off to resume play.

At that moment, I couldn't imagine loving him any more than I did then.

When Dr. Buchhalter phoned, he suggested we change the ratio of the diet to the highest ratio possible. If that didn't work, he wanted to consider an anti-seizure drug called Lamictal which wasn't available for use until recently.

"This medication is hard on the liver. We need to check liver enzymes every couple of months." He concluded.

Within twenty-four hours Susan had emailed the new menu and it was started. Because of Christina's still loose muscle tone, the physical therapist didn't think her head would support a helmet. Instead, we removed all of the hard toys near her and padded everything in her path.

Along with the change in the diet, I emailed, telephoned, and spoke to everyone I knew and anyone who would listen to pray for our daughter.

As the season changed—when blazing red and orange leaves drifted to the ground, and the air smelled like leaves and warm apple cider, our family too was entering a season of change. Within twenty-four hours of changing the diet, the seizures decreased their frequency. Seven days later, they had stopped.

Larry and I decided not to say anything to anyone, not even to our daughter's new therapists, until we had several weeks and knew for sure the diet had worked. Larry and I thought we had seen a change in Christina's alertness and behavior, but we were careful not to jump to conclusions. When the fall air began to turn frigid, visible clouds of breath could be seen as Terri and Sarah arrived for an appointment. After removing coats and rubbing cold hands together, they began working with Christina. I knew they were using their God-given gifts and tutelage for special needs children. It showed in their knowledge and handling of our daughter. They never ever tired of trying the same thing over again in order to help Christina understand. Both worked hard to help Christina understand sign.

Later, Mathew watched through a window as Larry's shrinking car rolled down the long dirt driveway. The thin road swam through rows of corn stubs sticking out of the snow covered ground. Mathew watched out the window until he was out of sight, and then sat down in the living room to play with a truck. In the kitchen, I began spooning Christina's ketogenic breakfast of unsweetened peaches, egg, and whipping cream into her mouth. In between bites, I signed for more.

"Do you want more?" I urged with a yawn.

Looking into the dish, I scooped a piece of fruit and brought the spoon to her mouth. I froze, my eyes shot to her hands as her little fingers touched, and then to her face. She moved her hands midline again—this time it was trenchant—and deliberate.

"Oh my gosh, she is signing." I half whispered, half gasped. Barely holding my excitement, I yammered, "Do you want more?"

Christina clearly pressed her hands together forming the sign again for "more."

"Ha! Christina—you understand! You're communicating!" I cheered.

She smiled back and flapped her legs, as if to say, "Give me more food!"

Upon hearing my lyrics, Mathew rushed into the kitchen. He stared open mouthed as she signed. Profuse joy filled the air as she continued with each bite of food to ask for more with her hands.

"Yeah-oh, yeah!" Mathew danced recklessly, twirling while putting his hands together in the sign for more. This was better than the best Christmas present—ever.

Christina's Early Childhood Teacher, Carissa Applebaum
during her last year in preschool

Chapter Sixteen
Freedom and the First Sound

Seizure-freedom is like warm ocean air brushing your face as waves lap at your feet planted firmly in white sand. –Paulette George

TRIUMPHANT.

There was no other word to describe it.

As weeks formed into months without a seizure, we knew the long journey to find seizure relief was over—all was calm.

Though we had moved from our first home in Minnesota, to Texas, and from there to this Illinois farmhouse to find seizure relief—we were about to move again—but happiness consumed us because Christina was seizure-free.

A year after we moved to Illinois, the office Larry worked in was closing and Larry's boss Phred asked him to move to the home office in Wisconsin. At first I objected, it was too much moving, too unsettling for the kids. We had even begun to make plans to build again in this small town in Illinois, but Larry now worked for a good company and the owner, Phred, was an honest and ethical employer who genuinely cared about the people who worked for him. We didn't want to give that up and Larry wanted to stay with this company, feeling he had a future there. Once again, we packed. This time we only packed the belongings that weren't already in boxes and moved to Wisconsin.

Our new home, nestled between woods and preserve land, was just blocks from Lake Michigan. From our backyard, off in the distance, we could see the enormous lake and hear the hum of jet skies and motor boats as they moved along the water.

As I stood in the yard of our Wisconsin home and smelled the cool oak and maple trees that filled the woods surrounding us, I recalled Roger and Terri's visit to our new home in Texas—and that traumatic first seizure-filled hospitalization. Our family had changed since then. But now two years later, the seizures were gone and instead of leaving our friends to be at the hospital with Christina, we were able to spend time together.

The blustery Lake Michigan shoreline with its sand and waves recalled Corpus Christie and our last visit to that much warmer gulf. At Corpus, we let Christina play on the sand because we knew that if she seized there she would not be hurt. Here on the shores of Lake Michigan, we let Christina play in the sand— because she enjoyed it. She was autistic and developmentally delayed. But we now had hope.

During a follow-up visit with Dr. Buchhalter, he was pleased with the seizure control Christina had, but the Lamictal had caused her liver enzymes to elevate. He decided to begin slow removal of it—miniscule increments so as to not disturb the balance we had achieved with the ketogenic diet. It took months, but when it was completely removed Christina remained seizure-free. And—on its own—the ketogenic diet alone controlled her seizures.

Six months later, Christina had a follow-up appointment with Dr. Frederick. When he entered the waiting room with her file in his hand and called her name, she turned to look at him.

"Christina—is that you?" he stated with a surprised smile. "It's remarkable—she looked at me when I called her."

He screened her development through questions and personal interaction with her. And though she was still more than
two years delayed, he wrote in his notes, "autistic symptoms are
not evident, it's quite miraculous."

———◆———

The new world of IEP's.

We had never heard the words Individualized Education Plan
until Christina entered the special education program at the local
school district. But we quickly learned that this was the contract between us and the school district in regard to her "special" education.

On our daughter's first day of preschool, I held Christina's
little hand as we crossed the asphalt parking lot of school. The
Wisconsin sun was still warm and I was sweating—both from heat
and anxiety. Her thin, blonde teacher, Mrs. Applebaum, waited at
the door. As the children assembled in line, Christina's lips protruded and she cried. I faked being cheerful.

"Mommy will pick you up when class is over, okay?" I said
wiping her tears.

Mrs. Applebaum smiled at me, "It will be okay—I'll take good
care of her." As she escorted Christina down the hallway, Christina looked back at me through tears and held her pointer finger
and pinky up trying to form the sign for "I love you."

I signed back, "I love you."

Maneuvering through cars in the parking lot, I began to cry—
like most mothers might on the first day of school but I had additional concerns. My daughter couldn't speak and I was fearful something might happen and she wouldn't be able to tell me. I wondered
if Christina was really even aware of her environment. Many of the
students seemed much older and more aware. Before the session was
over, I raced back to school early and waited for the door to open
and Christina to come out. Tears of joy flowed from both of us as I
rushed to pick her up. A routine we both quickly adjusted to.

The IEP required quarterly meetings to discuss progress. While Larry and I sat across from therapists and Christina's teacher, they read their evaluations and reports. Just like the report we had received from Dr. Frederick with the autism results; the reports drew tears and were at best disheartening. The impact on Christina of time lost developing—was painful. It was during these times that I realized Carissa Applebaum was a person lovely inside and out. She became a strong advocate for our child who would do whatever she could to help us help our daughter.

She allowed me to share our faith and belief in the ketogenic diet. And no matter what we saw on paper, we kept our feet firmly planted in belief that God was still in the business of healing. Even our entire daughter—development included.

Since moving to Wisconsin and meeting parents of special needs children, some whose own children suffered from seizures, I was able to share Christina's story. I had hoped that by sharing our struggle to find the right help, I could help others. At times our telephone rang with the voice of an anxious parent crying out for help. Many times they calmed down just knowing they were not in this alone.

When a friend of mine asked if I would talk to a young mom whose two year old son had been air lifted to the hospital due to seizures, I wasted no time calling. We met a few times, and I shared our story. She wanted her doctor to put her son on the diet and asked if I would come with her to the neurology appointment. Once there, the neurologist said her son could not go on the ketogenic diet.

When I asked the reason, the doctor said plainly, "It wouldn't help him."

"Why?" I inquired.

The doctor's back stiffened and he placed one leg over the other as he sat and said, "because it won't."

His defensive stance made me uncomfortable, but I inquired

again, "Why?" When I asked again, I obviously angered this doctor with my query.

He coiled his face back and said, "What are you...a doctor?"

When I explained that I was a friend who had a daughter on the diet, he dismissed anything I had to say.

"What was good for your daughter doesn't mean it's good for everyone."

I left his office that day wondering—was it because he didn't have a ketogenic dietician or did he simply disregard the ketogenic diet as a viable option?

This young friend did not know what to do. Her insurance had referred her to this doctor and taking her son anywhere else would cost her money she just didn't have. I urged her to seek help for her son somewhere else but found out later that nothing was done and he continued to have seizures.

I realized the journey to seizure-freedom was not just a hard one for us. It was everywhere—the resistance from the medical community to prescribe the ketogenic diet was both baffling and disheartening.

A mantle of snow covered the evergreen trees and was a smooth layer over the driveway and streets when a milestone and the holidays converged.

Silver and gold stars sparkled with glitter. Christmas trees dangled from the ceiling on red and green yarn. Christina wore a blue jean dress and held a piece of chalk in her left hand. I'm not sure what she was drawing but I loved it. Dangling from her arm was a silver medic alert bracelet. Inscribed on it was her condition: "seizure disorder."

She halfway turned toward me and she said, "mmmaammaa." I lowered the camera.

"Did you hear that?"

She said a word. It was like a melody we had longed to hear—her voice—a word. I whispered so as not to distract her from saying another one, "She's speaking."

Carissa came over and so did one of our daughter's therapists. They too had heard her speak. When my eyes met Carissa's, both of our eyes welled up with tears.

Years before I had sat on the floor of our home in Texas, face to face with Christina, mumbling, and modeling words. She looked away, but I followed her face with mine and begged her to form a sound, any sound. Now, today, she spoke clearly. My heart was full. Our three and a-half year old, Christina, was forming sounds for the first time.

Two years seizure free.

By the time Christina turned four years old, she was living proof of a ketogenic miracle.

My journal read: "We started the appointments with an MRI...she has to have an IV for sedation...this is the worst for her. EEG again with sedation, blood work and kidney and liver ultrasounds. Her last appointment was Friday—it took an entire week. But we had the best news from Dr. Buchhalter."

Was this real? Two triumphant years of seizure-freedom were done. We had done all that was necessary, we evaluated what was possible, and decided we needed to move, and we *had* achieved what seemed impossible.

Now, as we sat on the long benches in the patient room, it was as if we were on the field of a sporting event, waiting for the clock to tick zero and the officials to declare us victors. We were triumphant—we had won.

Dr. Buchhalter smiled at us. We were anxious to hear the test results but his attention was on Christina. He watched her as she shifted her attention from her musical toy to him. Her eyes widened as he opened his black satchel. She was curious about what he was doing. I expected him to remove a stethoscope or reflex hammer but instead he pulled out a beige rattle. Christina reached out for it and grabbed it, shaking back and forth, listening to the scrape of the pellets inside. Dr. Buchhalter smiled again and reached into his bag for another toy. Christina took it as well and began playing with it, dropping the rattle to the ground in her excitement. Dr. Buchhalter seemed to be enjoying himself – he played with Christina as if she were the only person in the room. He played like a parent, not a doctor – as if this was his new child. And in a sense, she was. Christina had never interacted with him like this before. She'd never been aware enough. The diet had made her new.

Still sitting he explained, "The EEG looks good, really good. There is some mild slowing in the background but nothing alarming."

"Is it possible to start removing the diet at this point?" Larry asked.

"I think it is entirely possible. She has been seizure free on the diet just short of the two years which is recommended. Plus, she has been on this diet since she was very young. It's entirely possible that the diet has done its job. However, we should slowly wean her off," Dr. Buchhalter replied.

At first, removing the diet was an uncomfortable thought for me. It was her medicine. She had been on it since she was ten months old. It was like an old friend; one who was moving away—I had to say goodbye and it was bittersweet.

This particular trip to Mayo Clinic was over my birthday. After the appointments were done, Larry surprised me by picking up our nephew Seth in Stillwater to stay with Mathew and Christina while we went across the street for dinner.

The restaurant was dim, lit by the star-like flickers of yellow candles. Larry and I chatted about Christina's positive appointment and the answer to our prayers. This dinner felt like a celebration of the end of a long journey.

As we ate our dinner—the food tasted better. I had an appetite that had been lost in the anxiety and fears of the last few years and ate as if food were new to me. The waiting staff was extraordinarily attentive—

it was a bit odd, in fact, because the waitress, after we'd eaten, hovered near the table as if she were waiting for something. "Waiting for what?" I wondered to myself as I placed my napkin on the table.

At that moment, Larry reached down and lifted his jean high enough to pull a long thin box from his cowboy boot. He handed it to me with a coy smile.

I looked at him in wonder, "What is this?"

He smiled, "Just open it."

The waitress brushed tears, and I realized he had told her in advance of his plan.

As I lifted the cover off the long gold box, a gold and diamond bracelet glittered back.

I drew in a breath, and looked at my husband whose face was now beaming.

"Happy Birthday, Honey," Larry said.

I was surprised at the beautiful bracelet. "I love it, but we can't afford this, can we?"

Larry's face became soft and his eyes moist, "You are a good mother. You've done everything you can to help our daughter and you've managed to take good care of Mathew too. I love you."

I didn't know what to say, but hearing my husband say those words, brought tears to my eyes and I reached over to hug him.

As we traveled back home from Mayo, we began talking about what it would be like for Christina to be able to eat different foods.

"Mom?" Mathew asked, "Will she be able to eat pizza?"

Larry grinned, "Well, son if she likes it—she's a George and we all like it. So I'm sure she will." Mathew smiled.

Violins and fiddles played as we danced in our seats heading south on Hwy 52 which wove into Hwy 94 that threaded us up and over the rolling hills of southern Minnesota and over the blue ripples of the Mississippi River and into Wisconsin.

Chapter Seventeen
Good Morning, Beautiful

Beautiful music is the art of the prophets that can calm the agitations of the soul;
it is one of the most magnificent and delightful presents God has given us.
–Martin Luther

SOME STORMS PROVIDE HOPE. AS Larry drove our van
home from Rochester, we saw one such storm. Wind was rocking
the van back and forth as dark cumulus clouds dropped raindrops
that shattered against the windshield.

Larry hunched over the steering wheel, trying to see the road
in front of him when Mathew shrieked, "Mom, dad, look!"

I was just about to scold him for yelling while dad was driving
in a storm—when I saw what caught his attention. A gap in the
clouds, a tear in the darkness, and light-rays of sun-light filtered
down. But it was more than white light. In the midst of them was
a magnificent hemicycle of colors, flung into the sky by divine
hands, spreading impossible colors against the monochrome sky.
Mathew's nose and open hands pressed against the window. Wonder shone on his face at the rainbow of promise appearing in the
midst of the storm.

Whenever Whitney flew in, she warmed our home. She had
turned fifteen during the summer and now had a womanly face.
When she arrived at the house, she rushed into the kids' room

and began to play. Though she looked like a young woman, her energy for play had not diminished. She flipped Mathew on her legs, somersaulting him over her Barbie-doll ponytail. He landed on a mattress, waiting for his fall. Christina liked this sight and squeeled, "Eeee!"

After they tired of that, Mathew and Christina performed the song Christina was learning in her preschool class.

"If you're happy and you know it, clap your hands." Mathew would clap, and Christina followed along clapping once. When the song continued and they came to the part, "if you're happy and you know it, your face will surely show it…" Christina put her fingers to her cheeks and said, "shuu, shuu, shuu."

Later while Whitney rocked Christina, she pushed her lips together and I noticed she was fighting back emotion.

"Whit, what's wrong?" I asked.

Emotion began to drench her face, "Will she be able to talk like other kids?"

I understood Whitney's cause for concern. At more than four years old, Christina did not come close to the development of other kids her same age. It was evident in her speech. Larry and I had to make a choice each day to remain hopeful. Whitney and I talked about God, and our belief that He was still in the business of healing. The healing for our daughter that our family prayed for was not just for her physical healing. It was also her whole healing.

I wrapped my arms around Whitney while Christina scrunched between us.

⊸≡⊷≡⊸

As soon as the new menu had arrived from Susan, we began incorporating the changes into Christina's ketogenic meals. Green snap covers and clear containers were scattered around our kitchen, as Larry stacked beets to weigh on a gram scale with the care of a jeweler.

He commented, "Doesn't it look like a lot more compared to what she was getting?"

The smidgen more of beets would never have been noticeable to the average eater filling a plate, but for a person on the ketogenic diet, a smidge more or less mattered. To us, it did seem like a lot. We had governed her meals meticulously since she had been on the diet since she was ten months old—it was her seizure medicine. Any adjustments to the diet usually meant a reduction. Now, with two years of seizure-freedom, the ratio of her diet is changed and she will be getting more food.

While Larry helped to prepare her new menu, a white towel flopped over his shoulder. He weighed and measured foods on the gram scale. Wiggling his shoulders and smiling, he made silly faces and noises rejoicing at where we were in the journey. I smiled at his silliness. The increase in food for our daughter was the sign of success—it was cause for celebration!

Within a week of changing the ketogenic ratio of Christina's diet, the celebration ended.

With pillows scrunched behind my back, I lounged on the bed reading. Christina had drifted off to sleep for her afternoon nap just inches away from me. When her eyes sprang open, it surprised me. I watched for a second thinking she was dreaming. I called her name. She didn't acknowledge my voice.

My heart raced and I called Larry, "Pappa (as Mathew began calling him)." A familiar fear crept inside of me. A knowing, that I did not want to acknowledge. Larry sat on the edge of the bed and spoke to Christina, calling her name. She did not respond. He snapped his fingers. She did not acknowledge.

"Something's not right." I brushed my hair back with my hands and held them atop my head. I could feel myself breathing far too rapidly.

Larry frowned and sprang back at what I implied—refusing to think it might be a seizure. "She's dreaming. She has to be dreaming."

The behavior continued. In hopes we could blame this on an ear infection, which had in the past woken Christina, I took her to the pediatrician. When he finished examining her and found no infection, I described what we had witnessed.

The tall male doctor shook his head, "That's not a seizure. They don't look like that. She's just waking up from a dream— probably the change in her diet was causing this."

Without any further discussion, I thanked him for his time. Inside of me, the part that no one sees—the part that sensed a storm coming before—knew better. Tears clipped out of my eyes as I blinked driving home. The doctor's position, felt uncomfortably familiar. I was being told everything was okay, when my insides told me differently. This doctor was not a neurologist. Yet he offered his expert opinion in regard to seizures. I just wanted him to check her ears.

As Christina began her second year of preschool, the EEG confirmed seizures. Dr. Buchhalter changed the ratio of the ketogenic diet back to 4:1 in hopes it would again stop the seizures. Not long after school began, I waited on the sidewalk against the brick wall of the school building for Christina's class to be dismissed. Instead of my daughter coming to the door to be let out, Mrs. Lesnik, the teaching assistant, motioned for me to come into the building. My heart sank when I saw Mrs. Applebaum scrunched down on the floor. Her arms wrapped around my daughter, half on her lap, as she contorted forward with a seizure.

I gasped and ran to them.

Mrs. Applebaum looked up with distraught eyes, "Why aren't they stopping?"

I knelt and hunched over Christina, making sure she was breathing and began the all too familiar task of timing the seizure. When it finally ended, two minutes later, all the other preschool children had been led to their parents. The hallway was empty and quiet. Florescent lights flickered above as we huddled on the floor. The emptiness in the hallway mirrored my feelings. I was excited and joyful just two weeks ago. Now, I lacked those positive emotions—and even anger failed to form in my chest. I was empty and numb.

Had time gone backwards? It seemed we were in the same dark place we had been two years ago. There had been no warning sirens this time. Dr. Buchhalter was again manipulating the diet and adding medication to try and stop the new reign of seizures. Christina broke out in a rash. Medication had to be changed, and our lives became changed once again.

Even with the new therapies, the seizures became relentless and more aggressive than before. Christina usually woke when one began. She would wrap her fist in a grasp, grind her teeth—choke and stop breathing. In between gurgling and grinding sounds, I would beg her to breathe while holding a phone in my hand and 9-1 already pressed. Despair and depression were oppressive enemies of the soul that I fought off after each one.

Larry and I tried to make sense of it all. We flashed back to those first seizure-filled days when Christina's lovely young babbles and coos went away. We feared it would replay—the seizures, the hospitals, the silence.

I was grieving the loss of seizure-freedom, unsure of what to do next.

Feeling far away and unheard from God, I questioned Him, "Why are they back? I don't understand—didn't our miracle diet work?"

Silence.

I knew He was there and will never forget when he told me so, out loud in the bathroom of a hospital. But, now, here in the midst of this renewed horror, I wanted to hear from Him. I wanted the seizures to stop.

Solemn and depressed, I quietly folded jeans fresh out of the dryer. Mathew and Christina were playing on the soft carpet of our master bedroom. The buttons clicked on Christina's musical toy, and piano cords from another toy mixed. When I noticed there were no sounds, I turned toward the bedroom door. I worried for a moment that Christina might be having a seizure. When her little round head peered out the door, I was relieved. She stood for a moment as if listening to something—then trotted past me. I set the jeans down and followed her.

"Nina, (as we began to call her) where are you going?" I knew she didn't have the words to tell me, but I hoped she would stop long enough for me to catch up to her. She ignored me and sprinted clumsily. She was making sounds and seemed to be intentional about them. I couldn't make out her jibberish. *Was she mumbling?* She stopped in front of the cabinet door which held the stereo system. She took hold of the knob and pulled the door open. I'd never seen her do anything like this before. I assumed she heard music but, *did she even know what the stereo was?* The muted sounds of piano and lyrics came out from the speakers. These sounds didn't carry into the laundry room. But somehow they did to Christina. She continued to babble again.

As her sounds continued, I began making out what I thought were words. The same sounds she had made, played back to me through the speakers in the form of lyrics—song lyrics. Her sounds were words—strung together. Something she had not been able to do before. At nearly four and a half years old, the only sounds we had heard from our daughter were one syllable, maybe two of maaammm or daaadd and Maphh, for Mathew.

I held my hair back with one hand and leaned into the speaker to hear closer.

When the song chorus repeated she followed along, much to my surprise.

Christina sang, "Mornbufilll ho wazzz yo niiiihhh mii wazzz wonflll."

My eyebrows raised and my jaw dropped as I watched her mimic these words. Christina's arms flexed and swung in a show of happiness toward the music.

As the chorus repeated, "Good Morning Beautiful, How was your night? Mine was wonderful."

Her little legs began to march in place and she extended her arms toward me to be lifted up. I pulled her up and sat her up on my hip, letting her legs dangle off to the side. She bent over and reached for the stereo with great effort. I wasn't sure what she wanted, but assumed it had to be the song. I twisted the volume knob to the right and the music carried through our home. She squealed with delight in my arms and kicked her legs.

There was renewed hope in her cognitive ability that up until this moment hadn't been there. Her words came so slow, but now that she had connected the lyrics, hope that she would speak in full sentences became immense. For me as her mother, it was a huge victory knowing that with repetition, our daughter was learning.

The radio announcer blared, "That was 'Good Morning Beautiful' by Steve Holy, now climbing the charts in the #20 spot."

That evening after Larry had come home from work, I told him about Christina's rush to the stereo to listen to this song, and how she repeated the words to the chorus—together. We waited for the song to play again, and when she heard it, she ran to the living room. We watched as she squealed with delight and repeated the words again to the chorus. Out of all the songs that had played, she picked this one as her own.

At nearly four and a half years old, during one of the most tumultuous seizure filled times we had known, Christina showed us nothing was impossible when she repeated the words to this song. It was as if God said, "Let there be light," right there in our living room.

A rainbow was a promise to humanity that God would never again punish the earth with a flood. The storms had rolled across our family and even now continued to batter us with rain—but Christina's song was a rainbow. The song was a glorious splash of color and hope in the midst of trying times.

Christina, 4 years old, hospitalized for SISCOM testing. The gauze head wrap covered the EEG electrodes.

Chapter Eighteen
The Ketogenic Miracle

"Our greatest weakness lies in giving up. The most certain way to succeed is always to try just one more time."—Thomas Edison

I HAVE BEEN TOLD THAT difficult times can be faced with strength if we know God. One does not discover this without experience. It's the sort of truth that we bob our heads in agreement with, but do not understand until trials come. Larry and I, at this point, needed a strength that was not our own, and we knew where to find it. We had seen His rainbow of promise and were confident that we were not alone.

At a quarterly meeting with the teacher and therapists from preschool, the recent developmental reports were disappointing. But as Larry and I sat on chairs at a long square table, Christina's teacher Carissa smiled positively. She slipped a yellow sheet of construction paper from a folder and slid it over to us. We both smiled when we read the letters: c-h-r-i-s-t-i-n-a, perfectly formed. Our daughter had written her own name. A Pulitzer Prize winning writer could not have written a more beautiful word.

In the six weeks since the return of Christina's seizures, she'd been hospitalized three times—the first two accomplished nothing

to help us exterminate the seizures. She'd had intricate EEG's and been monitored. During her third hospitalization, Dr. Buchhalter led us to the epilepsy monitoring unit at Mayo Clinic's Methodist Hospital for SISCOM testing. While SISCOM sounds like a NASA orbital platform, it stands for: Subtraction Ictal SPECT Co-registered to MRI. It is designed to pinpoint the location of seizures. Dr. Buchhalter called these locations "hot spots."

The area for SISCOM testing reminded me of a science fiction movie. Flat screen monitors wrapped a wall near where nurses sat. The monitors flashed images of the eight rooms that connected to this central hub. Some of the monitors displayed indecipherable graphs from EEG's running.

"Here we will monitor Christina," the nurse explained.

Before settling our daughter into her room, 32 electrodes were placed onto her head for the EEG. Christina objected by waving her arms and moving her head from side to side. She had to be held, and struggled in my arms. When they were on, a lab technician worked to insert the IV. After the technician struggled to place it, I requested a pediatric specialist to try. Christina took in ragged breaths and hiccupped back tears by the time we finally sat on the bed in her room. As she settled down, Dr. Buchhalter came in.

"I hear it's been a rough start," he said, pulling up a chair at the end of the bed.

I was glad to see him and anxious to understand how it would all work, but before we discussed anything, Christina stiffened with a seizure.

Dr. Buchhalter looked at his watch and began timing. The electrodes were in place, and the EEG was monitoring her, but without the IV, the dye could not be injected for the test.

Dr. Buchhalter observed as the seizure continued.

When it was over, Dr. Buchhalter spoke to the air as if someone else was in the room with us. "Did you get that?" he said loudly.

"Yes, we got it," echoed a voice from a speaker.

I wiped Christina's tears and comforted her. She smiled when I kissed her and almost as though she didn't realize he had been in the room, put her hand out to her doctor. He reached both of his hands to her and cupped it between his as she regained consciousness.

Through emotions I whispered, "We have to stop these!"

His eyes softened and he nodded his head. "You look tired."

Although I'd slept well the night before, I felt weak. Exhausted from something we had already lived through. Had we not already lived in hospitals? I didn't want this to be. She was seizure-free, once. But now, here we were once again. Christina and I were at the hospital without Larry or Mathew. I was tired from the newness of a storm we believed was done. I cried.

Dr. Buchhalter waited, holding Christina's hand until we could converse.

"If successful in pinpointing the seizures, we might have an opportunity to surgically remove that area of her brain." Dr. Buchhalter spoke with hope, that this would be an option.

"Please, try to get some rest. You both need it."

Christina's nurse came back into the room after he left, this time with a new technician.

The technician smiled at me and Christina, "I'm going to attempt to place the IV and do it as quickly as possible, okay?"

She started by talking directly to Christina, first catching her attention. The IV slipped in the first time and it was over.

When they had left, I took Christina's hand in mine and prayed. She was quiet, tired from the seizure as I spoke out loud to the Lord:

"Father, I lift Christina up to you. Thank you for her and for giving her to Larry and me. As hard as it is to imagine, we know that no one loves her more than you. Please help us now. This is hard. Bless the doctors with wisdom that they need to help our daughter. We pray for healing, in Jesus name."

Christina finished that prayer for me, "AAmmeen!"

Early the next morning, another seizure began. Within seconds the door burst open. Four nurses came rushing in. Without speaking, one cleaned the IV and another opened a vial and put the syringe into it. She pressed the syringe and injected the pre-measured supply of radioactive dye. A voice talked over the intercom giving information to the nurses present.

The nurses monitored Christina's heart rate and breathing while she continued through the seizure. Then we waited until the seizure dissipated.

The voice came over the intercom again, "We got it!"

Minutes later a sedative was injected into the IV.

Once sleeping from the sedation, Christina was wheeled onto a gurney to the CT (computerized tomography also called CAT) room where another team of nurses and doctors were waiting. It occurred to me that this was like a well orchestrated play. Each one knew their part, and did so without discussion because it had been so well rehearsed.

The nurses left, one by one, as the CT staff and doctors took over Christina's care during the testing. As the staff walked away, they gave each other high-fives and back-slaps. This wasn't callous behavior on their part. They were just proud of themselves for having captured the seizure and injecting the dye at the right time. My mind was focused on our daughter, but I was truly thankful for the nurses and staff who did their job well.

While waiting for Christina to have her scan, I grew aware that my daughter had radioactive dye pouring through her veins. This is something a parent would never think about, much less consent to. I prayed that this test would help her, not harm her.

The next day one last scan was done while Christina was not having any seizure activity, in order to compare the images.

A day after the tests were completed, Dr. Buchhalter tapped at the door and stepped into Christina's room. He looked especially doctor-like that day with pens bunched up in the pocket of his grey suit and an armful of EEG printouts and other technical-looking documents. He smiled broadly as if he had some good news. He closed the door and pulled a chair up next to mine.

Carefully – and acrobatically – Dr. Buchhalter managed to pull a stack of x-ray film from the stack of papers without tossing them across the floor. He held the film in front of me as if I would immediately see the significance.

"If you put the images on top of one another, they all show the same thing," he said in a conversational tone. He seemed excited. "The seizures are originating from the area in her right temporal lobe where the lesion is—we can see it clearly!"

"What does this mean?" I asked him.

"For the first time, we can explore surgery as an option," he answered.

In the past, surgery was not considered because the seizure activity was generalized (in all areas of her brain).

"What about the other parts of her brain?" I asked.

"Nothing, there is no seizure activity showing. We only see activity from the right temporal lobe with a large focus coming from the area of the lesion."

We looked at each other. A smile shyly crept across my face. While brain surgery was an extreme solution – it was a solution. I feared brain surgery, but it was exciting to hear that only a *part* of Christina's brain was showing seizure activity. It meant that – instead of being mostly sick – she was mostly well!

"The ketogenic diet—was this due to the diet?"

"There is no doubt that the seizure-free time she had on the ketogenic diet is the reason we are seeing what we are seeing now," Dr. Buchhalter nodded confirming.

"I am going to recommend surgery. But this decision is not mine alone. There will be a panel of doctors who will review Christina's file, and they will thoroughly discuss all the details and options before making a surgical decision of this magnitude."

———◆———

It was Thanksgiving week when Dr. Buchhalter called with the news of the panel's decision—surgery had been recommended.

For Thanksgiving, we drove to our friend's home in Madison. Lolly and Drew had built their home on a high area that overlooked a patchwork of farm land and acres of trees and evergreens. The cold November wind had torn most of the leaves from the trees, leaving only vivid green pine branches that whipped in a brisk wind. The air was cold and abrasive and not at all hopeful.

I smelled the aroma of roasting turkey and cooling pumpkin pies, but felt none of the warm cheer that usually accompanies the Thanksgiving holiday. I did not feel thankful: my daughter's seizures had returned and she might need brain surgery. I was petulant, distant, and tearful. But they say that the best friend is one who still loves you when you are unlovable. I sat in the kitchen with Lolly, a woman I'd known since I was 17 and discovered what friendship was. They understood what I was going through. They had also seen the miracle of the ketogenic diet. So, instead of returning my sentiments to me, they prayed for us and offered us love and grace. Slowly, my hope returned. The diet had revealed the lesion and Christina might yet be healed.

———◆———

The next week we packed for a return visit to Mayo Clinic to meet with the surgeon. It was during this time that my mom was the most help. She had now been living between my sister Jenny's house and ours for the past few years. And even though Mom's memory was failing, she loved to sit and watch her grandkids play. It allowed me a bathroom break or a shower. I was struck that even though her memory was fragile, much of the time, when she was with the kids, she resumed the role she had always known to be hers, a mother.

"Paul, come here," Mom called.

Hearing her voice, I rushed into the living room where I found Christina pushing Mathew over. Her hands were on his chest and he was flailing his arms around, laughing, and having a good time.

"She is just fine—there is nothing wrong with her," my mom stated.

When she had called me by the name Paul, I remembered the day when I went into labor at the airport. When mom kept saying, "that baby is not going to wait!" she was certain Christina would be born on the floor of the airport terminal. But now, she didn't remember any of that. But she did know her grandkids in front of her—and today I thanked God for that.

Relentless nighttime seizures caused Larry and me to have Christina sleep with us. Sleep was light and many times, I would wake and nudge her to make sure she was okay. When she moved, I thanked God for another day with her. Each morning, I would lie on my pillow and face hers, listening to her quiet breaths— thankful she was breathing. When her eyes opened, I would sing, "Good Morning Beautiful, How was your night?"

One morning, she woke and I was still half asleep next to her. She flinched a little but didn't move from her position. My eyes stayed closed in hope of just a moment longer of rest.

When her little voice uttered, "Beafifl," I knew she wanted to hear "her" song. I could hardly contain my emotions through a raspy morning voice as I began to sing "her" song.

"Good morning, beautiful, how was your night? Mine was wonderful with you by my side. When I opened my eyes to see your sweet face, it's a good morning beautiful, day."

Christina and Dr. Buchhalter

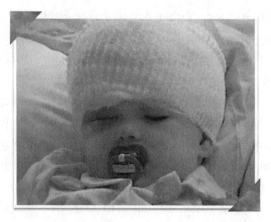

Christina, four-and-a-half years old two days after brain surgery.

Chapter Nineteen
The Christmas Gift

"Faith is a living, daring confidence in God's grace, so sure and certain that a man could stake his life on it a thousand times." - Martin Luther

I'M NOT SURE WHY THE rocking chair was the first thing Larry and I purchased when we discovered that I was pregnant. Most couples would have purchased a crib or a highchair. But Larry and I bought this wooden chair with its sanded curves and chestnut brown finish that had been with us as long as Mathew. This is why in the days before surgery, Christina, Mathew and I sat together, rolling back and forth, wrapped in the warm embrace of a knit blanket. The chair made me recall the pregnancy—how excited we were, how gravid my body felt. Back then, we had no idea that we'd be holding our daughter in this rocker through the most threatening time of her life. Stroking Christina's blonde hair, I closed my eyes for a moment. The thought of surgery made me feel torn between the desire to protect and the wish to save.

Christina wiggled down, and Mathew and I followed her unsteady toddle into the living room. I heard faint music coming from our TV, which had been accidently left on when we left the room. She squeaked happily—she'd heard her song all the way from the other room and had come in here to listen to it.

I wondered why she was so enthralled by the singer's voice. But there's not necessarily an explanation. When I was young, I took comfort in hearing my grandmother's voice. Now, I love to hear Mathew's wild laughter when Larry tickles him or my husband's deep voice when he says, "I love you." I cannot explain the rapture of these sounds—but I love them, just as Christina loves, "Good Morning Beautiful."

The surgery was approaching but, nevertheless, we danced in our living room to "Good Morning Beautiful."

Christina's neurosurgeon was taller than I expected. But his height was disguised by the warmness of his smile and the humility of his manner. Dr. Raffel was a professor of Pediatric Neurosurgery. He had taken Christina as his patient and had made a thorough examination of her brain scans in preparation for his surgical recommendation. He seemed trustworthy – but we were shocked to hear what he had to say.

"The entire, right temporal lobe?" Larry exclaimed, his face wide with surprise.

"Yes, I am confident that this will give her the best chance of success." He leaned forward a bit. "When we look at the images, the one taken during a seizure shows the entire right temporal lobe—lights up. Doing this procedure will give her an increased percentage of being seizure free."

Seeing our reluctance, he looked at us kindly but with confidence. "I won't do surgery unless we remove the entire area—it gives us a better chance to stop the seizures."

I felt numb the rest of the meeting and had to fight tears and emotion in order to think as the meeting progressed. It was explained that Mayo Clinic had done their first temporal lobectomy ten years prior. Christina, however, would be one of the youngest to have the procedure done. The risks were discussed: Death.

Bleeding. Brain damage. There was also a 20% chance that she could lose her memory—the things she loved, her music, Mathew, Larry, and I could be lost from her memory. None of it was a risk we wanted to take. Although Dr. Raffel was careful to inform us of these risks, he also gave us hope. Hope that through a successful right temporal lobectomy, there was a stronger than 60 percent chance that she would become seizure-free.

It was a grueling decision. One that, just like having children, didn't come with instructions. We prayed, we cried, and we watched the seizures rage. When we decided to allow the surgery, our days filled with apprehension of what was to come.

When surgery was scheduled for December 21st, we realized that Christmas would be different this year. I purchased smaller than usual toys so that the gifts for the kids could be easily transported. And with my mom's help, all the presents were wrapped and under the tree two weeks before we had to leave for the hospital.

I called and emailed as many people as I could think of to begin praying for Christina's surgery. I even emailed the local radio station, asking them to keep playing, "Good Morning Beautiful," but asked most of all for prayer. I didn't think the station would ask for prayer for our daughter, but I sent the email anyway. I found Steve Holy's website, the singer of "Good Morning Beautiful," and sent an email of thanks for such a great song. When an email landed in my inbox asking me to share our daughter's story, I did. Within 24 hours, a recap of our daughter's struggle with seizures was posted to the front of the singer's website. People from all over the world emailed me notes of support and prayers.

Larry's mom met us in the hall of the surgical area, and some family members gathered in the waiting area. Some drove hours to come to the hospital to be there for us. When Christina was taken into anesthesiology, they asked for only one parent to go.

"I'll take her," Larry said. "I don't make many appointments; I should do this."

The double doors of the surgical hallway swung solemnly closed behind my daughter. I felt as if the surgery on Christina were a surgery on myself and that, if anything happened to her, it would happen to me as well. Rubbing alcohol wafted in the air, making my stomach upset. I rocked a bit in my chair, staring at the scuffed tile floors. My four year old was going in for brain surgery. I cried. Nurses asked me if they could help. But what could they do? What could anyone do?

When Larry returned to me, his face was streaked with tears. Sobs disturbed his normal strong, unmoving chest. He said nothing as he grabbed my hand. We walked through the hallway, passing the playroom with Mathew and family members. He didn't notice us. I was thankful—I didn't want him to see mom and dad like this and upset him. We wandered further aimlessly until we came to a bathroom. Larry pulled the door open and closed it. We faced each other and wept.

"She just looked at me when they put the mask over her face." The pain on his face—it was as if he had betrayed his only daughter. "What if something goes wrong?"

Our wet eyes met. I spoke quickly, "Let's just go and get her. They'll understand. We will tell them—this will have to wait until we can handle this."

We took a step toward the door—and stopped. Breathing heavily, we knew our emotions were violent strangers. Unable to think, unable to choose, we knew but one person who could help us now. We lifted Christina to the Lord.

Carol Kent wrote in her book, *When I Lay my Isaac Down:*

> "However, most of us will face an 'Isaac experience,'
> when a crisis is thrust into our lives without warn-
> ing and without survival instructions. Our 'Isaacs'

are the heart sacrifices we make when we choose to
relinquish control and honor God with our choices
even when all seems lost. We have to decide if we
will let go of our control over a person, situation, or
event, or if we will hang on for dear life and refuse
to relinquish something we cherish."

Christina was our "Isaac."

Still holding hands, Larry and I prayed, "Heavenly Father, we
lift Christina up to you. We ask that you take care of her. We
know that this is out of our hands. Guide the surgeon's hand and
give wisdom to the doctors. Help each person in the operating
room to do exactly what is right for her. Keep her safe. We trust
You, and we want Your will to be done. We thank You for Christina and ask once again for her healing. In Jesus name."

Larry reached for the towel dispenser and handed a towel to
me. We wiped off our faces and took many deep breaths until
hiccups and uneven breathing were gone. We opened the door
and went looking for Mathew.

"Mommy, Daddy, come look at this, it's so cool!" he said pointing at a truck in his hand. We both hugged him and held on to
him for a long while.

Seven hours after we left Christina in the surgical area, a male
nurse escorted Larry and me to a room in the pediatric intensive
care unit.

When we were finally allowed in to see Christina, she was
lying on her back in the bed with a large, white, gauze turban
engulfing her entire head. Wires were attached on her chest, arms,
legs, and neck. I pulled up a chair next to her bed and took hold
of her hand. Larry and Mathew stood at the end of her bed.

"When is she gonna wake up?" Mathew asked.

"I don't know honey, when the medicine wears off, I guess,"
I replied.

He came over to me and hugged me, then kissed Christina's hand. He wasn't afraid at all. The headdress did not faze him.

My body was feeling the lack of sleep from the night before. I felt heavy and dizzy. I put my head down on the bed next to Christina and went in and out of sleep for the next several hours.

I woke to Larry's voice, "Hey Hon, are you OK?"

"I'm fine—" just then Christina's hand began to move.

"Hi Pumpkin," Larry said touching her blanket covered feet.

We watched as she moved her head a tiny bit, then remained still. Her eyes opened by a tiny slit.

"Pappa, miii Daddee," Christina said groggily.

Both Larry and I looked at each other with tearful joy. In those three little words we knew that her memory was there. She even remembered—remembered who Larry was and what she and Mathew called him.

Dr. Raffel was pleased with how the surgery had gone and rejoiced with us that Christina knew who we were. It wasn't long before we were able to move from the intensive care unit and into a regular hospital room. When the child in the room next to us was discharged, her mother gave us a small Christmas tree with lights for our room. Larry set it on the ledge of the window and we tucked presents under the tree that we had brought with us.

Thirty-six hours after surgery, the bandages came off revealing an incision that both doctors had prepared us for.

When Dr. Buchhalter came to say good bye, he wasn't dressed in the usual suit and bow tie. I realized that the cable knit sweater and kahkis meant he was already on vacation.

"I couldn't get on the plane if I didn't know she was doing okay," he stated.

We had not seen any sign of a seizure since before surgery.

"Well, since there isn't anything left for me to do, I may as well leave huh?" he said smiling at Christina.

"Baaa byy." She managed as he waved to her.

He hadn't been gone for more than a few hours when a rash developed and had to be counteracted with medication. The anti-seizure drugs they had given her had to be discontinued. We were optimistic, but then she stared into the distance and didn't respond. The worst feelings imaginable—she had surgery and still had seizures.

Christmas would be spent here in the hospital.

We'd hoped for the best and received the worst. I didn't feel like celebrating—there was no holiday joy in my heart.

After Dr. Raffel observed one of the seizures, he wanted to know if they were like the ones she'd had before. They weren't—they were minor, in comparison. Instead of Christina losing control of her body, she would stare for a few moments before returning to us. Dr. Raffel seemed relieved. He seemed to think this was an improvement.

But Larry and I tortured ourselves with self-doubt.

"Did we just allow her to have this surgery for nothing?"

Larry groaned and bent over the chair. "This is not what she needs. Not after all she's been through."

There were only two other patients left during the holiday on our wing of the hospital: one child critically ill with cancer and another who had also had brain surgery. At a time when our pain was deep and piercing, I was able to cry with and be of comfort to another mother. We shared a common bond in pain and agony over our two children. Her daughter's tumor was removed, but she wasn't expected to walk. We didn't know all of the details, but Larry and I prayed in Christina's room for these children.

When carolers strolled down the hallway, my first thought was, *there are only three kids on this floor—they must not realize that.* The hallway filled with forty or fifty voices. When they stopped first at the door of the girl with cancer, then the girl next to us who also had brain surgery, I realized they had come here for the three patients. "We wish you a Merry Christmas, we wish you a Merry Christmas," rang throughout the hallway. Larry carried Christina and we gathered in the doorway of her room. They paused by our room and sang for a while. Christina's incision was swollen red with black stitches. Her face was swollen red and one eye swelled shut. My heart wasn't rejoicing; my mind filled with thoughts about the seizures. I was tearful and sullen.

Early Christmas morning, Christina had one moment of absence for a seizure.

Mid-morning, Dr. Raffel came in. "How is she doing today?" he asked.

"I reviewed everything, and I am confident with what we have done. Keep in mind, she was very swollen the day the bandages came off." He went on to remind us of something important. "These are not the same seizures she was having. You haven't seen any of those, right?" he asked.

"Right, these are completely different." I answered.

Larry and I felt reassured—we now realized that these seizures might be related to the surgery, the swelling that naturally accompanies such a radical procedure. The seizures were different, which meant that we may have done the right thing.

When sleigh bells echoed in the hallway, Mathew's eyes popped wide.

Three abrupt knocks on our door, "Ho, Ho, Ho, is anybody home?"

Larry and I looked at each other when "Santa," dressed in red velvet and white fur trimmed clothing and hat, asked for Mathew.

"Here, I'm right here!" he cried out.

"Well, that's good because I have something just for you."

Then Santa pulled out a large wrapped package with Mathew's name on it. When he finished opening his remote control car, Santa lay a wrapped gift gently on a somber Christina. Mathew helped Christina open her gift, and as I watched them, I realized that Christmas could be anywhere as long as we were together. Mathew helped her unwrap a baby doll. Then Santa reached down into his large velvet bag and picked up a wooden cradle. It was handmade for our daughter by volunteers for Mayo Clinic.

Not long after Santa left, the carolers stood outside of our room singing, "Silent night, Holy night, all is calm, all is bright."

Mathew said, "Merry Christmas!" Following his example, Christina, too exhausted to lift her head, said, "Meerr Kismss."

"God bless you!" someone yelled, and another one, "We are praying for you."

Their sacrifice of being here on Christmas Eve warmed my heart. I began feeling remorse for feeling so negative. I chose to celebrate the miracle of Christmas: the birth of a child who was to heal this broken and sickly world—that same child who would grow into a man and heal children much like Christina. Like Mary, I treasured those thoughts in my heart.

Neither Larry nor I knew at the time that this Christmas we would receive a special gift. A gift more priceless than the one we received two Christmases ago when our daughter began signing.

This Christmas present was the most special of them all.

The last seizure.

Steve Holy and our family.

Christina posing with her favorite picture of Steve.

Chapter Twenty
Miraculous Formation

Miracles are a retelling in small letters of the very same story which is written across the whole world in letters too large for some of us to see.—C. S. Lewis

MIRACULOUS.

No other word to describe it.

When the air flow is smooth and just right near Mt. Rainier, lenticular clouds form. These clouds form all over the world, but Mt. Rainier has been known for putting on a miraculous display of them. The smoother the air flow, the more dramatic and majestic the clouds become, from marshmallow créme saucers resting in the sky to majestic bouquet white shaving cream clouds that hover in stable air.

These magnificent cloud formations remind me of the calm without seizures. There is a smoothness that allows for miraculous formation. A formation that begins as a tiny grain of sand in an oyster that God fashions into a beautiful pearl. In contrast to the lenticular clouds which many times precede rain, there is no rain in our forecast.

Those first weeks and months after surgery, however, were a struggle. Christina scampered through the house often fussy. She paced as though she didn't know where she wanted to go. Not able to sit, she breathed anxious breaths. Thick tears wet her cheeks. I didn't know what to do, or how to comfort her.

"Nina, tell mommy—are you hurt, are you sick?" I would ask.

She didn't have the words. I would bend and look into her eyes, not seeing the healing red scar that swam behind her ear to the top of her head. I would see only my daughter's pleading eyes. When she flung her body into my legs grabbing with her hands, it seemed she was a mess of tangled emotions. Was it frustration, sadness, or pain? I lifted her into my arms and held her on my hip.

Turning the stereo on, we swayed. She sobbed.

We listened to music for a while. Christina continued to cry until I slid "Good Morning Beautiful" into the CD player. When the piano and violin whispered across the room, she began to calm and when the words she loved were sung, her head pressed onto my shoulder. She drew in ragged breaths until she was quiet and still. But when the song ended, she fussed for more. I replayed it several times. I smiled in wonder at the song, the voice—that calmed my spirited child.

Six weeks after surgery, Christina and I had not left the safety of our home. But now, now she was better and rambunctious and happy. We slid winter coats on and drove to a small western store. Brown saddles and western boots and hats were displayed in the window. The air was cold and fresh as I carried Christina into the store.

We were greeted by a woman wearing a long skirt and fancy stitched western boots. When I told her we weren't looking for anything special, I noticed her eyes gravitate to Christina's incision line. It was uncomfortable to look at, especially on someone so young. I began to tell her about the recent surgery, but she interrupted.

"You don't need to explain. We heard about her—she had surgery in December, right?" she asked.

I searched my mind for a moment, stunned that this woman knew of our daughter's surgery.

"Yes, but how…." I began to ask.

"We heard about her on the radio. They'd repeated it for weeks—we've been praying for her," She said.

The email I sent! I learned that while we were in the hospital, the Milwaukee radio station announced my request—asking for prayer. Strangers and people we might never meet were praying for our daughter and our family. In addition to that, our daughter's story remained posted to Steve Holy's website. Emails filled my inbox and Larry and I were touched by so many who cared. Their prayers meant the most.

When Christina returned to preschool, leaving her there was like her first day of school all over again. But now she had a scar, a grim reminder of the tumultuous past. Upon returning, her development was uncertain and scattered at best. The yellow construction paper with her name perfectly written was at home, tucked in a box of treasures to keep—but now, her formed letters were wobbly and stretched up vertically. Mrs. Applebaum was concerned. Christina did not follow along like she had before surgery and needed assistance to perform simple tasks that she had done before, like sitting in circle time or walking in line. Larry and I were concerned, but would not let our hope become dashed. Martin Luther King, Jr. once said, "Faith is taking the first step even when you don't see the whole staircase."

We did not see the whole staircase of Christina's life. What we did see did not lend us hope. But we believed that God was still in the business of healing. After what we had been through and witnessed with the miracle of the ketogenic diet, and God's gift to man of wisdom in neurosurgery—we would not give in, or give up. We held on to hope.

During Christina's first year of kindergarten, the awards ceremony was held in the gym of the school. The side door, not normally open, was for this event. As I walked into the brick school building,

I remembered back and I slowed my steps. My eyes lingered on the area of floor where Mrs. Applebaum held Christina during a seizure two years previous. But now the seizures were gone and the fear of what had taken place was a memory. I searched for two open chairs and waited for Larry. Kitty, our neighbor, found a seat next to mine. Her daughter Alex, whose curly black hair matched her mother's, is the same age as Christina. When we first met Kitty and her family, our two girls were three. Alex talked and played as little girls do, but Christina couldn't say mommy. Kitty said to me that she noticed Christina had changed, she was talking and developing.

Before the ceremony started, I scanned the room looking for Christina in a nest of chattering students and busy teachers. I finally saw her pink dress. She was sitting cross legged on the floor. I wondered what award Christina would be receiving. "Special kids" were sometimes given a generic award since their accomplishments were not always the same as other kids.

As the awards were announced, each student who received one walked to the stage, took the award from their teacher, and shook Principal Miller's hand. Then the kids would stand holding the award for all to see.

The room quieted as Mrs. Forrester began to announce the awards for her class.

"For overall academic performance, Christina George."

Felicitous tears of surprise came to my eyes. I had cried a lot during those seizure filled years, but these were tears of joy. Sniffling was heard among the audience and Kitty's wet cheeks reminded me that many knew our daugter's story.

Christina's purple shoes marched straight up to her teacher and she grabbed the award. She walked past her principal, forgetting to stop. Halfway to where she was to stand, Christina turned and came back.

She blurted, "oops, I forgot!" then shook his hand like a grown-up, as the audience crowd laughed.

After the ceremony had ended, and the crowd filed out of the building, I waited to talk with the teachers. Mrs. Applebaum, who had invested three years and instruction lovingly to our daughter, and I shared an emotional embrace. When I spoke to Mrs. Forrester, I had to ask if the award for overall truly meant what it had in the past, meaning overall—the entire class. In Christina's kindergarten class there were 5 or 6 special needs children, and the rest of the class of 20 did not have any learning disabilities. She smiled warmly, and what she had to say surprised me.

"This award is for overall academic performance," she formulated.

"Christina is as successful as any other student in my class. She's smart—and showing us what she can do."

This was the beginning of what we would soon learn about Christina. Our daughter was growing up to be an achiever and lover of knowledge.

That year, when Christina was six years old, the crucial window of time had passed. Most neurologists will say that two or three years of being seizure-free is a hallmark of success. She was seizure-free and growing tall. Christina began to make friends. The most important friendship of all is the one with her brother.

Mathew wrote: Mom was driving us to school, and there was a patch of trees on the road, the sun filtered through the trees flashing at us as we drove to school. Mom always said, "don't look at flashes of sun through the trees," because flashes are known to trigger seizures. When Christina was looking at them, I told her, "Nina, stop looking."

She whipped her face toward me and glared. Her nose scrunched and she squeezed her lips at me and said, "Mathew—stop tellin' me that!"

After that moment I realized, it was all over. Life was going to be very different. Christina was better.

We had purchased for the kids a plastic kitchen set, which included its own telephone. Christina often had the red phone pressed to her ear. She would strut through the house, chatting and discussing with a pretend friend. With her head bent to one side, she'd giggle and laugh as though deep in conversation. Abundant waves of hair covered the phone and the scar was now invisible behind the blonde strands.

"Christina, who are you talking to?" I questioned with a playful tone.

She put her pointer finger up as though she were telling me, "hold on one minute." I buried a laugh at her imitation of me. I had done that when either Mathew or she interrupted.

When I heard her say, "hello" it caught my attention and I gazed at her.

It wasn't just any "hello." It was her tone, and the background cords that struck a nerve in me. They were lovely and comforting and familiar. Our daughter, who did not speak for the first three and-a-half-years of her life, now spoke fluently as well as used simple sign language. But that's not what caught my attention—it was her voice.

I said to her, "Christina, say hello again."

She happily obliged and when she did, I realized God had blessed her with a special voice—and it was a sweet gift to me. My daughter's voice—had the same pitch, same ring, the same tone as my Grandmother's. When Grandma would answer the phone, she had a distinct ring to the back of her voice. Christina's voice has the same beautiful ring. God in his perfect plan wove into it the gift of a voice that I loved and missed and longed to hear.

During fourth grade, Christina continued to prove she was an achiever when she made honor roll for the first time.

In early 2010, just before Christina's 12th birthday, we had our last IEP. For the past few years, the school district kept Christina on a consult due to such significant developmental delays she had had. But finally, during this last meeting, they concluded there was nothing more they could do for her. One therapist stated something Christina's doctor had said, "The file no longer matches the patient/student."

Christina loves school and math in particular—and she is good at it (she certainly didn't get that from me). She writes her name with perfectly formed letters, now in cursive. No longer on yellow construction paper, they are on lined notebook paper. She types (almost as fast as her mom) and she's learning Spanish.

Shortly after school began this year, she tried out for the volleyball team. Sports are competitive at her school and since she had not played before, the coach placed her on the team as a manager, to attend practices and learn the game. When an opportunity arose for the team to split into two smaller teams, to take on another school, the coach put Christina in to play. I sat high up on the metal bleachers, nervous and anxious for my daughter's first appearance on the court. Mathew and I took hands and prayed for her success. It reminded me of years earlier when he prayed with me after she fell down the flight of stairs in the old farmhouse. My son was older and this time, he led part of the prayer.

When the coach called Christina, the court seemed to quiet—the girls on the team jumped from their seats and cheered, "Yeah—Christina! Go Christina!"

I wanted to cover my eyes fearing the worst, that is, I now feared she would miss the ball when it was her turn to serve. Christina's first hit went straight up into the air and hit the ceiling. The rules permitted her one more ball. The coach looked at Christina and nodded her head as though she were confident in our daughter.

Christina took in a deep breath. She positioned her legs, eyed the spot where she wanted the ball to land, and lowered her ponytailed head to keep her eye on the volleyball. When she served—the ball went over the net landing in an open area she had hoped it would. Her team cheered. She smiled satisfied at herself. I fought off emotion, not wanting anything to stop me from clearly seeing her serve the next ball. Mathew grabbed my hand and squeezed it in excitement. Through serving during that game, Christina scored a total of 11 points out of 25. Her teammates gave her a standing ovation when she finished.

Excited parents who didn't know our daughter said, "Who is that girl?"

Other parents, who are friends and whose daughters are friends with Christina, hugged and congratulated us. I emailed Dr. Buchhalter to tell him of the game she played and his email response was this: "I am very proud of her for just being on the team, manager or player, with or without points."

As I finished the last chapters of this book, my mind was engrossed in an emotional paragraph when Christina bounded into the room. She knew I was writing and stood silent waiting for my attention. When I looked up, she smiled as though she had a very important idea or was about to announce the discovery of a new invention. The suede-colored wall contrasted my daughter's tall frame. Long locks of heavy blonde hair curled around her face.

Her nail polished pointer finger tapped the palm of her hand and she asked, "I need your agent's phone number."

I gulped.

I wasn't thinking I was in any position to refer my novice daughter to him. But, I delighted in the thought of where she was going with this. I held off chuckling at her adorable appearance and steadied my words, "Why, would you want his number?" I queried.

Christina was very serious. "Well, I have written a story about a girl. And, I need an agent to send my manuscript to a publisher."

My mouth opened, but words evaded me. She had heard me, and remembered what I explained about the writing business. She did get something from me—not math, but the love of stories. It ran through my mind and my heart glowed, I love her.

I convinced her that her literary talents would need some refinement, as do mine, and that I would send Les, my agent, an email for her. Happy with the result, she wiggled in next to me and spied the computer screen reading some of her own story.

Then in a rather instructional tone she said, "Uh, mom, you spelled Mt. Ranier wrong. It's R-a-i-n-i-e-r."

After her correction of me, she jumped up and skipped to her room. I thanked God she gets A's in spelling and for spell check.

I did as I promised and emailed Les, who I'm sure smiled when he read my request. He quickly emailed back recommendations for the start of Christina's literary career.

After that conversation with Christina about writing, I paused to think back to that first seizure torn year of life until now. Her healing is miraculous. She inspires us every day with her presence, her life. She inspired me to write this book.

Not all seizure-stories end this way, and if it would be possible that hers when told, could change just one—that is our hope. Our prayers have changed. We no longer pray for her healing; we pray for those who might be reading this story—for you, and for those who have seizure torn days.

I thought to myself as I turned back to the computer. Our family's journey to get Christina better taught us how to hope—and how to trust in God's plan. I wondered after that conversation with Christina, if part of her miraculous formation would be to write someday, or sooner. Was that what God planned for her future?

Perhaps, instead of being the story Christina, our miracle will write a story.

Appendices and Services for Families

THE CHARLIE FOUNDATION TO HELP CURE PEDIATRIC EPILEPSY
www.charliefoundation.org
The Charlie Foundation has a listing of providers who administer the
ketogenic diet across the globe. Click on the hospital tab on the main page
for a complete listing of those providers.

MATTHEW'S FRIENDS
www.matthewsfriends.org
Helpline Numbers: 0-788-405-4811, or 0-785-006-2339
Email: eng@matthewsfriends.org
Information and support for parents of children who are on the ketogenic
diet, or for parents who are thinking of starting their child on the diet.

**Below are some of the Hospitals that provide excellent ketogenic
care and autism support:**

PHOENIX CHILDREN'S HOSPITAL, COMPREHENSIVE EPILEPSY PROGRAM
Dr. Jeffrey Buchhalter
*http://www.phoenixchildrens.com/medical-specialties/childrens_neuroscience_
institute/programs-services/ped-epilepsy-program.html*
602-546-1000
1919 E. Thomas Road
Phoenix, AZ 85016

MAYO CLINIC, PEDIATRIC EPILEPSY/NEUROLOGY DEPARTMENT
Dr. Elaine Wirrell and Dr. Katherine Nickels
http://www.mayoclinic.org/epilepsy/children.html
507-284-2511

200 First Street S.W.
Rochester, MN 55905

JOHNS HOPKINS, COMPREHENSIVE EPILEPSY PROGRAM
Dr. Eric Kossoff
www.hopkinsmedicine.org/neurology_neurosurgery/specialty_areas/epilepsy/
410-955-9100
600 N.Wolfe Street
Baltimore, Maryland 21287

MASSACHUSETTS GENERAL HOSPITAL IN BOSTON
http://www.massgeneral.org
617-726-2000
55 Fruit Street
Boston, MA 02114

CHILDREN'S HOSPITAL OF PHILADELPHIA
Dr. Christina Bergqvist
www.chop.edu
215-590-1000
Center Boulevard & S 34th St
Philadelphia, PA 19104

MONTEFIORE MEDICAL CENTER
Dr. Karen Balaban-Gil
www.montefiore.org
3415 Bainbridge Ave.
Bronx, New York 10467

LE BONHEUR CHILDREN'S MEDICAL CENTER
Dr. James Wheless
http://www.methodisthealth.org/lebonheur/
901-287-5437
50 N. Dunlap Street
Memphis, TN 38103

GREAT ORMOND STREET HOSPITAL IN LONDON
Dr. Helen Cross
www.ich.ucl.ac.uk
0-207-405-9200
London, WC1N 3JH, United Kingdom

Epilepsy foundations and research foundations:

Epilepsy Action-UK
http://www.epilepsy.org.uk/info/ketogenic.html

Epilepsy Information Services
National Society for Epilepsy
Chesham Lane, Chalfont St. Peter, Bucks SL9 0RJ
Epilepsy helpline: 0-149-460-1400

American Epilepsy Association
http://www.epilepsyfoundation.org
On the main page of this site is an area to key in your zip code, it will bring
you to your local Epilepsy foundation.

http://cureepilepsy.org
Cure is a nonprofit organization dedicated to finding a cure for epilepsy by
raising funds for research and by increasing awareness.

http://www.icepilepsy.org
(ICE Alliance) Intractable Childhood Epilepsy. ICE is dedicated to improving
the outcome for all treatment resistant epilepsies in childhood.

http://www.epilepsy.com
The Epilepsy Therapy Project brings together financial resources, scientific
insights and business expertise from leading academic and commercial
industry participants.

Other resources:

http://www.myketocal.com
by Nutricia North America. This website is a resource for dieticians and
clinicians interested in the ketogenic diet.

http://www.autismndi.com
ANDI is the Autism Network for Dietary Intervention. ANDI provides help
and support for families using a gluten and casein free diet in the treatment
of autism and related developmental disabilities.

Books:

Seizures and Epilepsy in Childhood: A Guide for Parents. Written by Professor John M. Freeman MD, Dr. Eileen P.G.Vining MD, and Professor Diana J. Pillas. A John Hopkins Press Health Book.

The Ketogenic Diet: A Treatment For Children and Others With Epilepsy. Fourth Edition. Written by Dr. John Freeman, Dr. Eric Kossoff, Jennifer B. Freeman, Millicent T. Kelly, R.D., Published by Demos Medical Publishing, New York, N.Y. 2007.

Seizures and Epilepsy in Childhood: A Guide for Parents. Written by Professor John M. Freeman MD, Dr. Eileen P.G.Vining MD, and Professor Diana J. Pillas. A John Hopkins Press Health Book.

Keto Kid. Written by Dr. Deborah Snyder, DO, published by Demos Medical Publishing, New York, N.Y. 2007.

Epilepsy and the Ketogenic Diet. Edited by Carl E. Stafstrom, MD, PhD and Jong M. Rho, MD, published by Humana Press, Totowa, New Jersey. 2004.

Unraveling the Mystery of Autism and Pervasive Developmental Disorder: A mother's story of research and recovery. Written by Karen Seroussi, published by Broadway Books, New York, 2002.

A Different Dream For My Child. Written by Jolene Philo, published by Discovery House, Grand Rapids, Michigan. 2009.

Good Morning, Beautiful. by Paulette George, published by Ambassador International, Greenville, South Carolina. 2010.

Support for families living with life-limiting conditions:

Faith's Lodge—serves families who have a child with a life-limiting condition, as well as parents and families who have suffered the loss of a child.

www.faithslodge.org

6942 County Road C,

Danbury, WI 54830-9763

Phone: 715-866-8200

Brave Kids— Organizational mission is to help children with chronic, life-threatening illnesses or disabilities.
www.bravekids.org

DR. BUCHHALTER OFFERED PRICELESS ADVICE throughout our journey to help our child. The following is his advice to *you* should you find yourself in a seizure storm:

If you have a child or any other loved one suffering from uncontrolled seizures, seek out and find the optimal care with the assistance of your local care providers, if possible. Frequently, the most comprehensive care for individuals with epilepsy is found in specialized pediatric and adult epilepsy centers. Sometimes the challenge is just getting there.

PAULETTE WOULD LIKE TO INVITE YOU TO VISIT HERE AT HER WEBSITE:
www.paulettegeorge.net

VISIT STEVE HOLY:
http://www.steveholy.com/

During a return visit to Texas six year old Christina danced on the floor of Gruene Hall with Mom and Mathew.